TYPEWRITING
AND
OFFICE DUPLICATING PROCESSES

Typewriting
and
Office Duplicating
Processes

by

A. W. Gardiner, F.I.R.T.

Associated Electrical Industries Ltd.
Rugby, Warwicks, England.

COMMUNICATION ARTS BOOKS
Hastings House, Publishers
New York

PRINTED AND BOUND IN GREAT BRITAIN BY

A. Wheaton & Co., Exeter, Devon

CONTENTS

PREFACE

The technology and equipment availability in the field of type-writing and office duplicating is advancing so rapidly that it becomes impossible to prepare any comprehensive work on the subject that will not be quickly outdated. However, this has not deterred me from including information on current equipment as a means of illustrating technical data which may not be superseded quite so rapidly.

In compiling this data I am greatly indebted to many persons and organisations for expert advice and, in some cases, permission to use extracts and illustrations from other original works. In particular, grateful thanks are expressed to Mr. D. P. Brooks, M.I.R.T. of 'Uneoprint', The Gresham Press, Unwin Brothers Ltd., for much of the information included on electric typewriters and mechanical attachments; to Mr. J. A. Young, F.I.R.T. of Ellams Duplicator Co. Ltd. for information on duplicating inks and to the Imperial Type-writer Co. Ltd., for the advice on stencil cutting contained in their booklet "Stencil Cutting and Hints to Typists" by Mr. W. H. Hollis. I am also greatly indebted to the Editor of 'Reproduction', for permission to reproduce extracts from an article on costing which I originally prepared for that journal.

A great deal of assistance has also been gained from other journals covering business equipment; in particular 'Business Systems and Equipment', 'Office Equipment News' and the 'British Printer' and grateful acknowledgements are extended to their respective editors.

As the Institute of Reprographic Technology are hoping that this book will take its place in a series of instructional works being prepared to cover the whole field of reprography, I am sure that its officers will also wish to join with me in thanking all concerned for the assistance given. This will be especially so when thanking my employer Associated Electrical Industries Ltd., Rugby, England, for the facilities made available to me for testing and research. Coupled with this I must thank my colleagues at AEI for a great deal of practical assistance.

In writing this preface after completion of the book, it is difficult to be sure that one has not overlooked someone to whom thanks are due for assistance in some aspect of the work. I trust there are no such omissions but if there are, I hope an apology for the oversight will be accepted.

Throughout the task of collecting subject matter for the book, all the trade houses contacted have been most generous in providing data and illustrations. They are listed below and I thank them all for their kind and courteous assistance:

Typewriters

Adrema Ltd., Friden Ltd., Imperial Typewriter Co. Ltd., IBM(UK) Ltd., Integrated Data Processing Ltd., Logabax Ltd., Moseley Manufacturing Co. Ltd., Office and Electronic Machines, Olympia Business Machines Co. Ltd., Remington Rand Division Sperry Rand Ltd., Smith-Corona Ltd., Ultronic Data Systems Ltd., Varityper Ltd.

Office Duplicating

Geo. Anson & Co. Ltd., Addressograph-Multigraph Ltd., Admel Int. Ltd., Block & Anderson Ltd., Copycat Ltd., A.B. Dick & Co. of G.B. Ltd., Eichner (Gt. Britain) Ltd., Ellams Duplicator Co. Ltd., Gestetner Ltd., Hall Harding Ltd., Ilford Ltd., Minnesota Mining & Manufacturing Co. Ltd., Office Machinery Ltd., Office Mechanisation Ltd., Ozalid Ltd., Rank Xerox Ltd., Roneo Ltd., Rotaprint Ltd., Shannon Ltd., Skycopies Ltd.

Last, but not least, I must thank my fellow councillors of the Institute of Reprographic Technology serving on the editorial committee for the time they have spent in reading and assessing the usefulness of the work to students of reprography.

CHAPTER I

TYPEWRITING

In many fields of reprography the student does not need to become a craftsman in a particular process himself. He merely wants sufficient technical knowledge of the process to enable him to apply it correctly and to see that his craftsmen have the most suitable equipment for their requirements.

Typewriting is one of those fields in which the reprographer is unlikely to be charged with basic training. He is, however, concerned with the product, especially when it is in the form of typescript for further reproduction. When this is the case he should be in a position to influence the whole typing operation including the acquisition of the most suitable equipment and the setting of standards of copy according to requirements.

There are two basic categories of typewriter composition determined by whether the typewriter is used to produce the printing surface direct, i.e. an actual duplicating master, or an image which is then processed by a reprographic method to create a duplicating master.

The first of these categories is usually described as direct typing, or direct image, and the second reprotyping.

All of the duplicating processes can be used with either category of typing but for direct typing the correct base material must be used according to the duplicating process chosen.

Type Size and Spacing

The conventional typewriter uses raised type and the typing is done in a single operation. After depressing one typekey and printing one letter, releasing the pressure on the key automatically moves the carriage and paper to the next letter space. The space for each letter being thus pre-determined, the characteristic feature of conventional typescript is that all letters or figures occupy an equal width which is known as unit spacing.

Conventional type is more or less standardised in three sizes; viz.

Pica at 10 letters to the inch; Elite, spaced at 12 letters to the inch and Micro-Elite spaced at 14 letters to the inch.

A system of measurement known as the point system is used to denote size of type. The idea was first conceived by Fournier, a French type founder, in the 18th century. He took a basic measurement of 2 inches and divided it into 144 parts and called each part one point. It was not until the latter part of the 19th century that America and Britain followed suit and accepted a points system based on Pica, the type size in most common use. This had a body depth of .166 inches and was divided by 12 to establish the point at .0138 inches (i.e. approximately $\frac{1}{72}$ inch).

Today the point system is used, not only to define type size, but also to indicate all parts of a setting such as size of spacing material, length of line and type areas. However, due to the difficulty of using such an awkward fraction as a unit of measurement, the practice has developed of grouping points in Pica ems, each em representing 12 points in length.

The depth of a line (i.e. from the bottom of one line of type to the bottom of the next) is usually one-sixth of an inch. For the easier reading of Pica type, however, it is desirable to have an extra line (double-spacing) or at least half a line (one-and-a-half spacing) between the lines of type, especially if the size is reduced in reproduction.

With Elite type, single spacing is usually satisfactory, because, with the same line-spacing (six lines to the inch) the proportion of letter height to line space is less than with Pica.

This means that on a printing surface of 6 in. × 9 in. (the space usually covered on a page of say $8\frac{1}{4}$ in. × $11\frac{3}{4}$ in.) 72 × 54 (i.e. 3,888) letter-spaces of Elite type and perhaps only 60 × 27 (i.e. 1,620) of Pica type are available, of which 5–10 per cent is wasted at the ends of the lines.

Many conventional typewriters can be obtained with letter spacings of either 10 or 12 to the inch; certain models are available with 8, 9, 14, 16, 18 and 20 to the inch letter-spacings, according to the size and design of type-face.

Line-spacing can be varied according to the number of teeth in the ratchet and, as well as the standard 6 lines-to-the-inch, spacings of $4\frac{1}{2}$ and 5 are possible.

The size of type must be related to the length of line and, therefore, to the size of the page. Small types are only suitable for short lines and small pages. There must also be a relationship between the length of line and the space between lines, because the longer the lines and the closer they are together, the more difficult it is for the eye to find the beginning of the next line.

According to certain experts in typesetting 10 point type (long Primer or petit Romain) affords the fastest reading and a line length of 80 mm is considered to be the one giving optimum efficiency in reading with this size of type.

As a rule longer lines have to be used for practical reasons. The use of a 7-in. (about 175 mm) line of Elite type does not cause serious objection but with smaller types a shorter line is advisable.

It is essential to give attention to this point if documents are to fulfil their prime purpose of being quickly and easily read, especially when the subject matter is of a technical nature.

Margins

The margin requirements vary according to the purposes of the documents. In the case of books, the binding margin must be sufficient to allow the whole of the page to be clearly visible, when opened. The right-hand margin (or on the reverse the left-hand) i.e. the front edge, must be sufficient to avoid any risk of "bleeding" the text when the book is trimmed.

One widely accepted formula states that the top and outside margins should be equal, the back margin should be one third more and the bottom margin about 7/6 of the outside margin.

Another preferred proportion is: top and outside margins equal, back margin 50 per cent more and bottom margin twice the outside margin.

In document reproduction the problem of the margin is not simply a matter of appearance. The marginal surface may be up to some 50 per cent of the textual surface. With photocopying, this can be expensive, as it may account for 20–30 per cent of the paper consumed.

Standards

Standardisation is a most important factor in economical production. It begins with the typewritten copy and should follow through all processes to final collating and distribution. In a central reprographic department the use of a properly designed order form should be insisted upon, and full information on the requirements of each reproduction job given in advance of work starting. Queries regarding requirements arising whilst work is in progress not only hold up work on the job in question but also disrupt the planned sequence of production throughout a department. A regular recurrence of such incidents can lead to a high degree of confusion, frustration and a lowering of standards generally.

Standardisation of the sizes of paper used for typing and copy making is obviously a very desirable practice. The International and British Standard sizes of trimmed paper for use in office stationery and printed matter are now based on the International Standards Organisation (ISO) A and B series of sizes. These sizes have the advantage that each is achieved by dividing the size immediately above it into two equal parts. The division is parallel to the shorter side, so that the areas of two successive sizes are in the ratio of $\sqrt{2}:1$. This means that all the sizes in the series are geometrically similar to one another (see p. 13). In each, the proportion of long side to short side is the same, the equation being:—

$$y : x = \sqrt{2} : 1 = 1.414 : 1$$

The ratio between the sides x and y is thus equal to the ratio between the side and the diagonal of a square.

The fact that each sheet size has the same aspect ratio is important to the reprographer because copy produced for one size can be optically reduced or enlarged to suit any other size in the series.

For example, drawings prepared on A2 and A3 sizes can be reduced to match the format of typescript prepared on A4, or alternatively all could be reduced to print out on A5 size.

The principal series is the A series based on the A0 size which has an area of one square metre. The B series is a subsidiary series intended for use only in exceptional circumstances when intermediate sizes are necessary. The B sizes are obtained by placing the geometrical mean between adjacent sizes, of the A series, so that the same proportions are retained.

The full range of sizes is illustrated on page 14.

Standardising on the quality of ribbons, paper and masters used for reprotyping assists in maintaining a consistency of image which, in turn, allows the introduction of standardised procedures in the reproduction stages.

As regards actual typing, the standard set will vary in different establishments but it is a good idea to provide each typist with a set of house rules laying down standards on such things as layout, margins, page numbering, consistency of spelling, abbreviation, methods of erasure, markings used in checking, etc. There are many

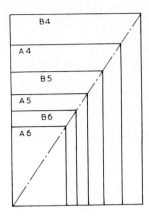

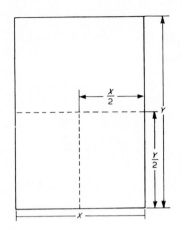

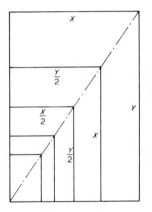

PAPER STYLES

(*Top left*) Relationship of supplementary B series to A series.

(*Top right*) The halving principle.

(*Middle*) An illustration of the geometrical similarity of sizes.

(*Bottom*) An illustration that the ratio between the sides equals that of the ratio between the side and the diagonal of a square.

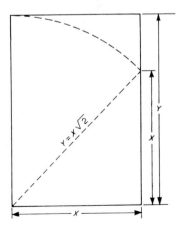

13

'A' SERIES OF TRIMMED SIZES

Designation	SIZE mm	inches	Designation	SIZE mm	inches
A0	841 × 1189	33.11 × 46.81	A5	148 × 210	5.83 × 8.27
A1	594 × 841	23.39 × 33.11	A6	105 × 148	4.13 × 5.83
A2	420 × 594	16.54 × 23.39	A7	74 × 105	2.91 × 4.13
A3	297 × 420	11.69 × 16.54	A8	52 × 74	2.05 × 2.91
A4	210 × 297	8.27 × 11.69	A9	37 × 52	1.46 × 2.05
			A10	26 × 37	1.02 × 1.46

'B' SERIES OF TRIMMED SIZES

Designation	SIZE mm	inches	Designation	SIZE mm	inches
B0	1000 × 1414	39.37 × 55.67	B5	176 × 250	6.93 × 9.84
B1	707 × 1000	27.83 × 39.37	B6	125 × 176	4.92 × 6.93
B2	500 × 707	19.68 × 27.83	B7	88 × 125	3.46 × 4.92
B3	353 × 500	13.90 × 19.68	B8	62 × 88	2.44 × 3.46
B4	250 × 353	9.84 × 13.90	B9	44 × 62	1.73 × 2.44
			B10	31 × 44	1.22 × 1.73

ways to do a job but there is only one way for each establishment. This way should be known and understood by everyone involved.

Output and Cost

It is difficult to state definitely what is the output of an average typewriter, or rather of an average typist.

Figures of top speed typists obtained in a contest (say some 500 typestrokes per minute) are of no value in this respect; not even the figures obtained by a time study of the working speed of a number of typists, timed by means of a stopwatch. The only figures of practical value are those obtained by recording data over a long period and including all losses of time caused by rest pauses, cleaning the machine, adjusting the manuscript to be copied, putting the copy material (including the carbon paper) into the machine, correction of errors, assembling the completed sheets etc., etc.

The results obtained vary widely and depend upon the skill of the typist, the difficulties of the manuscript, linguistic difficulties, mathematical or other formulae, tabulator working, etc. Rough estimates show that the output varies between 500 and 2,500 words per hour.

For calculation purposes it is better to estimate a moderate figure than a too optimistic one. These figures should be decreased by some 20 or 25 per cent if stencils or typewritten masters for offset or similar purposes are to be prepared. With the latter work it is essential for the typist to make few errors so that correction work is limited.

Another rather important labour-cost factor in excess of the pure typewriting is the additional cost of producing carbon copies. Per carbon copy an increase of 15 to 18 per cent may be estimated. This cost factor also depends partly on the number of corrections to be made.

Some interesting statistics have been published from time to time which reveal the high cost of typing, usually much higher than is generally appreciated. One consultant reported that in a firm where 50 executives initiated correspondence, the average daily output of typing amounted to 2,500 lines of type. This work load was handled by 10 shorthand typists each paid at £11 per week. Their individual rates of production ranged from 90 lines to 380 lines per day, but their average of 250 lines per day per girl was in keeping with findings in surveys carried out in other organisations. Within the firm in question a detailed cost study revealed that the true cost of each shorthand typist was £1000 per year. Each letter was costing more than three shillings, nearly fourpence per line not to mention stationery and the cost of dictator's time.

In a review carried out on a wider basis some years ago by a Management Association, average times were established for a 30 line letter of 15 minutes for dictation, 25 minutes for transcription by a shorthand typist and 20 minutes when copied or produced by an audio typist. The average total production per day per typist was assessed at 13 full pages but when this survey was undertaken an 8 hour day was usual and only stenographers of average and better than average ability were included.

The conscientious reprographic manager should obviously make every effort to see that the typing labour available in his organisation is used to the best advantage and not dissipated on non profitable tasks such as re-copying and making multiple carbon copies. Checking of their own work by typists should generally be insisted upon as this not only saves the time of the more expensive staff but also encourages accuracy.

Costs, Manual and Electric

Although in recent years many makes of electric typewriters have become available, the rate of replacement of manuals by electrics has hitherto been slow. This is mainly due to the seemingly high cost of electric machines, but when the extra cost is compared with the claimed production increases and savings brought about by the change, the economic advantages of electric machines are quite positive.

Savings of up to 30 per cent in typing time have been established where electrics have been used for specialised work and normal economies of 10 per cent are common. These savings almost invariably justify the use of electrics in place of manual typewriters.

A published example of change from manuals to electrics by one manufacturer, gave the following details. A typing pool of 20 typists costed at £15,000 per annum based on salaries and direct overheads was reduced to 17 typists saving £2250 per annum. Against this was set the cost of equipping the 17 typists with electric machines costing £1500. Based on a 5 year depreciation period on the equipment, it is estimated that £9000 would be saved over the 5 years.

From these figures it is concluded that increases in output as low as 5 per cent would make the installation profitable, bearing in mind the other benefits achieved.

CHAPTER II

TYPEWRITERS

Broadly speaking typewriters fall into two main categories, manually operated and electrically operated, but as many of the electric machines have manually operated features, perhaps it would be more accurate to describe the two groups as non-electric and electric. Although the British Standards Institute have settled on the terms manual and electric (BS. 2481 : 1961) some manufacturers refer to their manual machines as standard (i.e. not electric) whilst others classify their cheaper electric machines as standard and yet again manual is also used with reference to the hand operated electrics as opposed to tape operated.

Electric machines in turn are of two kinds, semi and fully electric. In a fully electric machine, both the typebar strike and the carriage return movements are powered. In the semi-electric, which is also called the electrically assisted, only one or other of these is powered, some manufacturers offering a choice on the same model.

The carriage right-to-left movement is operated by spring tension on all machines; it is only the return, left-to-right, which is either electrically powered or manual. Conversely, it is the typebar striking action which is powered or manual, the return in all cases being under spring tension. Leaf and coil springs are used in a number of movements on both electric and manual machines. Even on electric typewriters some movements are always mechanical, such as the touch and impression controls.

Several other movements or actions can be powered or fitted with automatic repeating devices, but the details vary considerably and do not warrant classifying.

To meet the requirements of British Standard Specification No. 2481, all electric typewriters should provide impression adjustment, automatic repeat of underscore, hyphen, and back space, automatic line spacer, and automatic carriage return.

Typing Action

Another grouping arrangement, significant to the reprographer, is by mechanical features or typing action. There are two classes, those machines having individual type bars and those having interchangeable type elements carrying the whole type font.

The typebar is, of course, the one used in the vast majority of machines today, and may therefore be called the conventional system. Typebars, each bearing a type slug with two characters on it, are arranged in a semi-circular type-basket: they strike forward to a common printing point at about the horizontal centre of the platen, but at rest they lie more or less horizontally so that the printed characters are in full view. Apart from the separate typebars and the front-strike action, the other feature common to all conventional machines is that the carriage, bearing the platen and paper, moves from right to left character by character.

There are two major type-element machines: one of the earliest, the VariTyper, and one of the latest, the IBM 72. In these machines, as the name implies, all the characters in a font are on one type element, which in the case of the VariTyper is a curved metal alloy segment, known as a type sector or shuttle, and on the IBM 72, a sphere called a typing head, or colloquially, a 'golf ball'. The VariTyper, in fact, provides for two fonts to be mounted on the machine together.

The principle is the same in each case: the key action registers the type element in two planes to bring the selected character to a common position. In what happens after that, however, there are two vital differences: the VariTyper has a back-strike action (a hammer striking through the paper from behind) and the IBM 72 a front-strike one; and in the IBM 72 the typing head itself not only moves forward to strike the paper but also moves from left to right along the stationary platen, whereas the VariTyper has a common printing point and the conventional sort of carriage movement, although it has rollers to feed the paper instead of a platen.

Despite these differences, the fact that these two machines have type elements rather than typebars is what matters most, because this gives them both the outstanding facility – easily interchangeable type fonts.

The basic movements of all typewriters control: (a) the registering of the paper or other image carrier, both vertically and horizontally, to a fixed printing point, except for the IBM 72, and (b) the presentation of the ribbon and the selected character to that point.

TYPING ACTIONS

Machine	Mounting of characters	Strike action	Printing point	Carriage
Conventional	individual typebars	front	fixed	moves
VariTyper	two type elements	back	fixed	moves
IBM 72	single type element	front	moves	fixed

Some actions are interrelated, e.g. the keytap operates the typebar, the ribbon and the carriage. For speed and ease of operation, other movements can be built into machines, and many of these, too, are interrelated. For instance, the carriage can be moved not only by the character keys but also forward and back space, tab and carriage return keys; the latter, where it exists, also advances the platen; and so on.

Electric Typewriters

The application of electric power brings about a great improvement in the typewriter, by controlling the movement of the carriage or, what is more important, operating the typebars. The advantages are obvious: the work is less strenuous for the typist, and the force with which the type strikes the paper can be kept constant to any degree required. This produces a uniform density of print, which is essential if further copies of good quality are to be made, whether by photographic or other means.

To obtain this evenness of impression with all characters, whether capitals, wide or narrow letters, or small punctuation marks, it is necessary to use more force with the letters of larger area, such as capitals, than with those of small area. With the ordinary typewriter this has to be done manually, and needs skill and experience, but with some electric typewriters different degrees of force for letters of different size are automatically provided.

Electric typewriters are particularly useful for reproduction work. To use them effectively, however, the typist must be accurate and confident, because at the slightest pressure of the type-key, the letter is immediately struck. There is no time for change of mind, nor chance of retrieving an error.

When one-time reproduction carbon ribbons are used on the typewriter, a really print-like effect is produced which adds greatly to the presentation of finished copies.

19

With electric machines, the highest degree of force makes it possible to obtain a larger number of carbon copies in one operation, but in the reproduction field this may be considered a limited advantage as it is cheaper to type a master and use a duplicating process when more than four to six copies are required. Interleaving carbons and copy paper is expensive in typing labour and correction of errors may add one or two pence to the cost of each carbon copy.

With the handy location of control keys on the keyboard, shorter typing strokes and repeat keys for underlining, hyphen, full-stop and space bar, the typist's finger travel is reduced and typing movements speeded. Many of the electrics also have a touch control fitting which enables the operator to transfer smoothly from manual to electric.

There is no doubt that electric typewriters will get smaller, lighter and cheaper. Machines which give proportional spacing will remain comparatively more expensive, but, for certain types of work requiring a high standard of presentation, the additional cost is worth while.

Listed below are some of the standard electric typewriters which will provide a high quality copy for direct typing and an acceptable

STANDARD ELECTRIC TYPEWRITERS

Name	Approx. Basic Price	Extra features
I.B.M. Standard D.	£182	Touch control. 1/2 space and 7 typamatic. Choice of ribbon.
Smith Corona 410	*£210	Expand and 1/2 space keys. Carbon ribbon. Push button erasing.
Smith Corona 250 Mk. II	*£105	1/2 space via split action bar. Snap-on facility for special characters.
Remington Model 25	*£194	1/2 space. Dual-rite attachment for bold effect. Impression variable caps/lr. case. Interchangeable type heads on bars to order, 'Ultratouch' system.
B. & A. Facit	£162	2 Tabulating systems, one with mechanical memory.
Adler 21C	*£204½	Carbon ribbon.
Imperial 660	£173	Touch control. Auto-feed ribbon loader and magic margin control. ½ space & 8 typamatic.
Olympia SGE 40	*£191	½ space £5 extra. Auto finger switching Fabric to Carbon ribbon.
Olympia SGE 30	*£115	A new smaller edition of the above.
I.B.M. 71	£182	Carbon ribbon. Interchangeable founts.

(See Chapter V for machines with more extensive facilities).

* Corrected price after devaluation of £ sterling (other prices are pre-devaluation and may also be subject to changes).

(*Top left*) IBM Standard D   (*Top right*) Smith Corona 410

(*Middle left*) Smith Corona 250 Mk. II   (*Middle right*) Imperial 660

(*Bottom left*) Olympia SGE 40   (*Bottom right*) Remington Model 25

SOME STANDARD ELECTRIC TYPEWRITERS

standard for reprotyping in those cases where proportional spacing is not essential. All provide at least 88 characters on the keyboard plus some automatic repeat keys for spacing and characters such as underline, hyphen, X and full stop. Impression control and automatic carriage return key are also common features.

Choice of Type Face

Buying a new typewriter usually involves choosing a type style. With some machines the choice is limited; with others it is wide.

When much of the typing will be in the preparation of duplicating masters the choice should be restricted to an open face style. Bold faces do not always reproduce satisfactorily when used on direct imaged masters and neither do the very small micro and condensed styles. For reprotyping one must also bear in mind the possible degree of reduction in size intended in the final copies. While most type styles in the 10 to the inch range are comfortably legible at a 30 per cent reduction, micro styles of 14 or more to the inch are not as satisfactory at any major reduction.

Apart from these practical considerations, preference for any particular type face is a matter of individual taste. Visual powers vary largely in different people; we must not, therefore, expect every pair of eyes to be equally attracted, or repelled, by the same type.

Some of the differing characteristics in type styles present practical as well as aesthetic considerations. The width of letters is a variation which affects the number of words which can be printed on a page. A type face can be used at a wider pitch than its normal rating but not at a closer pitch.

The body size of a type face is another variable within styles of the same point size. It is measured in terms of the height of non-ascending and non-descending lower case letters, e.g. x, and secondly of the width of the m (which determines the pitch). Some type faces having a large body size appear to be much larger than other faces of the same point size.

Another important feature, which has a particular significance in the line spacing, is the length of ascenders and descenders. There are five letters in the lower case alphabet with descenders, g, j, p, q and y, and six ascenders, b, d, f, h, k and l. When the ascenders and descenders are long, the white areas between lines appear to be greater, but on the other hand, the face is, as a result, small on the body.

22

ABCDEFGHIJKLMNOPQRSTUVWXYZ& ABC
abcdefghijklmnopqrstuvwxyz abcdefghijklmno

10 pt Garamond Bold (680–10B)

ABCDEFGHIJKLMNOPQRSTUVWXYZ& AB
abcdefghijklmnopqrstuvwxyz abcdefghijklmn

This is the new Pica Shaded face. It writes ten characters
to the inch, and is thus interchangeable with Pica or with
any other style having the same spacing.

abcdefghijklmnopqrstuvwxyz

ABCDEFGHIJKLMNOPQRSTUVWXYZ

Pica (10 – 1″)

ABCDEFGHIJKLMNOPQRSTUVWXYZ
abcdefghijklmnopqrstuvwxyz

Pica is the traditional style of type
which is used for general purposes in most
countries. Business letters, in particular,
are mostly typed in Pica. Long usage has
amply confirmed its suitability not only for
typing but also for many other requirements
such as manifolding, stencil-cutting and the
preparing of hectograph and offset masters.

EXAMPLES OF A POPULAR TYPE STYLE
(alphabets reproduced full size, text slightly reduced).

The contrast between the thick and thin strokes in a type face is
seen to be greater when the shading of the rounded strokes is of a
more vertical form. Bodoni is an example of this vertical shading as
compared with Garamond having a rounded and more gradual
shading. There is a modern trend towards shaded type faces on typewriters. They bear a stronger resemblance to printers' type, especially
when a carbon ribbon is used, and shaded Pica, Elite and Roman can
be ordered from some manufacturers.

23

Pica italic (10 – 1″)

A B C D E F G H I J K L M N O P Q R S T
a b c d e f g h i j k l m n o p q r s t

This type style will produce excellent master copies for
all types of duplication. It will produce six to eight
legible carbon copies.

Pica Gothic (10 – 1″)

A B C D E F G H I J K L M N O P Q R S T
A B C D E F G·H I J K L M N O P Q R S T

THIS TYPE STYLE WILL PRODUCE MASTER COPIES FOR REPRODUCT—
ION BY SPIRIT, STENCIL AND MULTILITH DUPLICATING MACHINES.

Pica Gothic (12 – 1″)

A B C D E F G H I J K L M N O P Q R S T U V W X
A B C D E F G H I J K L M N O P Q R S T U V W X

FOR ITS SIZE, THIS TYPE HAS A VERY HIGH STANDARD OF READABILITY . WITH
REASONABLE CARE, IT WILL PRODUCE EXCELLENT MASTERS FOR DUPLICATION BY
SPIRIT, STENCIL OR MULTILITH PROCESSES.

Elite (12 – 1″)

A B C D E F G H I J K L M N O P Q R S T U V W X
a b c d e f g h i j k l m n o p q r s t u v w x

Elite has the largest face that can be typed 12 characters to
the inch. The design of this type, its size and 12 pitch
spacing make it very useful to modern business organizations.

EXAMPLES OF SOME POPULAR TYPE STYLES

Alphabets reproduced full size, text reduced 30 per cent. All manufacturers offer their own particular versions of these popular type styles (the examples are from the Imperial range) and, of course, there are many other types in spacings from 6 to the inch to 20 to the inch.

24

Special Characters

The conventional typewriter is provided with 42 to 44 keys, two characters per key. With this number the 26 letters and their capitals, the figures and usual special signs are covered. In exceptional cases the number of different types may be extended and, of course, special characters may also be ordered.

When the number of special characters required is extensive and beyond the capacity of a modified keyboard or the various gadgets available for extending the typographic versatility of a machine, machines with dual keyboards are available, as well as the more ambitious electrical machines with interchangeable fonts.

In the semi-electric range there is a double keyboard machine – the Imperial Dual-Unit 458 – which has been designed primarily for typing mathematical formulae and technical data. It consists of two units built side by side with a single carriage which may easily be transferred from unit to unit. Thus, not only does it avoid the necessity of removing the typewritten matter from the carriage, but ensures smooth integration of narrative symbols in perfect register.

The Dual-Unit 458, is fitted with a power drive which enables the transfer of the carriage to be accomplished by the touch of a key. The machine can be supplied with a choice of type styles on the textual keyboard and a very large range of symbols on the other keyboard.

All dual-unit typewriters have keyboards to suit individual requirements and there is no standard keyboard, as almost every customer has different needs. The two 46-key, 92-character keyboards give a total of 184 characters.

Extra Characters

When purchasing a conventional typewriter with its customary 44 keys and 88 characters, it is possible to have a limited number of characters varied from the standard layout. In many cases the alternatives offered are not sufficient or suitable. It may be that some characters are required only occasionally and in such cases it is hardly worth while sacrificing some standard and useful characters.

There is an answer to many of these problems in special attachments and modifications which are available from certain sources.

On machines with typebars there is a considerable degree of flexibility, not only in permanently altering any type slugs on the standard lay, but also in the introduction of additional and interchangeable characters and even interchangeable typebars.

The I.B.M. Executive in particular has this facility of specially designed changeable typebars. The system is suitable only where a few extra characters are needed for occasional use. It is slow in operation because the escapement mechanism is not changed and the character must match the permanent unit widths on the escapement for that particular key.

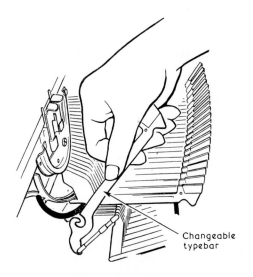

Changeable typebar

CHANGING A TYPEBAR

Mechanical Attachments

There are three attachments available commercially which are more flexible, all making use of the typebar striking action. Costs vary according to the number of characters needed and whether a typewriter mechanic is available to fit the various components, which can be bought separately.

In the *Typit* system a modified type guide is fitted to the machine permanently and acts as a holder for individual typits, which are 3 inch plastic bars in which are inserted small slides bearing the character required. The appropriate typit is inserted in the holder and any key (of the equivalent character width) on the keyboard is struck; the rising typebar strikes the slide from behind and the character on the front prints through the ribbon in the normal way; the typit is then removed and normal typing continues. Each typit

INSERTING A TYPIT
INTO THE TYPE GUIDE

carries one character on a specially made slide. There is a wide range
of characters available and the device can be used on all standard and
electric machines.

The *Alphamod* system uses a magnetic typebar holder supported
above the type guide by a tripod which is attached to the typebar
segment and therefore moves with the shift. It was designed for the
IBM Executive but can also be fitted to the Olivetti Editor.

Special typebars, called alphabars, placed on the Alphamod are
held in position by the magnet, and rest against a spring. Each
alphabar has an ordinary IBM slug mounted at its foot, and at the
top a small hole which fits over a spigot on the magnet. When an

$$\Phi \quad \propto \quad R_8 \quad \oplus \quad \angle\!\Theta \quad R \quad \ll \quad \gg \quad \$ \quad \spadesuit \quad \%\!\!/ \quad \rightarrow \quad \mathcal{A} \quad Y_\epsilon \quad \mathbb{B} \quad \P \quad \S \quad \tfrac{1}{8} \quad \S$$

$$\Box \quad \sqrt[3]{} \quad \partial \quad \text{\S} \quad \uparrow \quad \downarrow \quad \Omega_{10} \quad \neq \quad \Lambda \quad \odot \quad \mathcal{H} \quad < \quad \backslash \quad \cap \quad \pounds \quad \circledR \quad \chi^o \quad '' \quad \in \quad \hbar$$

$$\partial x \quad \geq \quad \eta\!\int\! \xi_{x+y} \cdot [a+b]^{-2\tau}, \; (\overset{...}{m} \rightarrow 0)$$

EXAMPLES OF TYPIT CHARACTERS

27

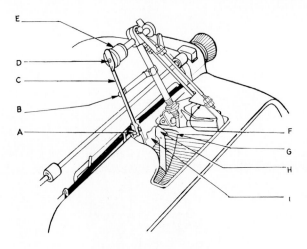

THE ALPHAMOD

A. Type guide. B. Spring. C. Alphabar. D. Spigot. E. Alphamod
magnetic holder. F. Masking cut away. G. Type bar segment.
H. Type bar in striking arc. I. Abutment ring.

alphabar is fitted on the Alphamod the character slug rests just in
front of the type guide. One of the permanent typebars is then used
as a hammer, in the same way as Typit, and the method of operation
is much the same.

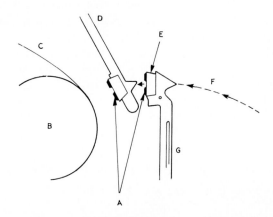

SECTION DIAGRAM OF ALPHAMOD

A. Characters (lower case). B. Platen. C. Paper. D. Alphabar.
E. Character slug. F. Striking arc. G. Type bar on machine.

GREEK α β γ Γ δ Δ ϵ ζ η θ Θ ι κ λ Λ μ ν ξ Ξ π Π

FOREIGN LANGUAGES pâté français straße señor

FRACTIONS, SIGNS & SYMBOLS $5^{11}/_{16}$ $\frac{7}{8}$ $3\,°C$ * † ‡ §

MATHEMATICS $\|x\|$ $\sqrt[4]{n+x}$ $\int_3^\infty$ R^{2n^2} x_{α_4} $z^{A^{m-4}}$ y

$$\sum_0^{p-\epsilon} P_{\xi\mu}\{i_{\xi\mu}(x,y)|>\epsilon\} < P_{\xi\mu}\left\{1 - \frac{1}{a\xi\mu(x,y)}|>\frac{\epsilon}{1+\epsilon}\right\} = P_{\xi\mu}.$$

EXAMPLES OF ALPHAMOD CHARACTERS

The third device, also designed for the IBM Executive, was originally developed for use in the American journal *Physical Review Letters* and has no special name; since 1959 it has been marketed by Mr. Fred *Paffrath*. It is similar to the Alphamod except that the extra typebar is held in a yoke and one of the permanent typebars (or two if four character widths are required) is fitted with a brass hammer slug. There are only a very few in Britain.

Extra Fonts

If you do not have a machine with interchangeable type faces, two alternatives are open for providing additional fonts on typebar machines.

First, you can change the type basket. It is possible on typebar machines to change the whole type basket or segment. This takes a little time and is normally a job for a typewriter mechanic but the Imperial Typewriter Co. used to make this a standard feature on their Model 66 manual machine. Changing from one interchangeable type unit to another involves only sliding the one out and the other into the frame. It is, of course, necessary that all the characters on the new segment have the same unit widths as on the replaced one. This is not an operation to be carried out every day, but it is feasible and may be a practical proposition in certain cases.

Secondly, a simulated bold face can be provided on the machine quite easily, and there are four systems for doing this, all by a second typing over the first with the register of the paper to the characters altered so that a distorted version of the ordinary face is produced. In two cases the distortion is vertical, and in the other two horizontal; three achieve this by moving the platen horizontally or vertically, the fourth by moving the type basket vertically.

29

The four methods are as follows:

1. *Betamod*

The Betamod is a simple modification to the spindle of an Executive platen. A lever moves the platen fractionally sideways and also disengages the platen advance mechanisms so that the paper does not advance when the carriage return key is struck after the first typing.

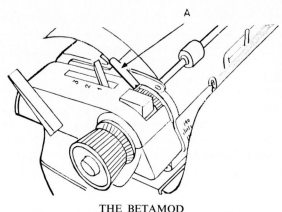

THE BETAMOD

This device provides horizontal distortion of typescript by fractional horizontal movement of the platen. A. Platen movement control lever.

this line shows the effect of HORIZONTAL distortion

EFFECT ON TYPESCRIPT USING BETAMOD

The amount of displacement determines the degree of boldness and is controlled by the thickness of the spacing shim fitted. The device is marketed by 'Uneoprint', Unwin Brothers Limited, Old Woking, Surrey.

2. *Cartoprint*

The Cartoprint boldening device also moves the platen horizontally, in this case the whole platen being displaced. The thickness of the character can be varied by a special lever. It is marketed by Cartoprint, Gl. Koge Landevej 119, Copenhagen, Denmark.

3. *IBM*

IBM have produced a new boldening device in Germany which is fitted as a modification at the time of purchase. A lever linked to the indexing mechanism rotates the platen fractionally, thereby producing a vertical distortion on the second typing.

4. *Doublebold*

In this device, the type basket is moved vertically by two micro adjustment levers. It was developed by Vance Weaver Composition Inc., and is marketed in America by Mechanical Enterprises, Inc., Alexandria, Virginia, and in Britain by the agents, Robert Maxwell & Co. Ltd., Oxford.

Other Bold Face Methods

There are in fact several other ways of achieving a simulated bold face, which is by far the easiest and most popular second face to produce. Those on the machine include using twin or double ribbons, or inserting some material like thick paper, film, etc., on the typebar side of the ribbon (perhaps operated mechanically). Both of these produce a thickened image on one typing which may prove satisfactory for certain needs.

Bold can also be produced by photographic methods. Blue gelatine over the words to be boldened reduces the exposure and consequently produces a thicker image on the negative. Alternatively, bold can be produced on the Optype optical photographic line justifying and composing machine.

The Optype can also be used to produce simulated italic, condensed and expanded – horizontally or vertically up to 12 per cent – versions of an original face, as well as reducing the size by anything up to 25 per cent. It is marketed by Logabax Limited, 21 Buckingham Palace Road, London, S.W.1.

No manufacturer of typebar machines seems to produce a satisfactory related bold version of a Roman face. One way of achieving such a face permanently is by filing down the surface of a Roman face. This needs considerable patience and skill, but it can work very well. There are one or two good related italics, in particular IBM's Boldface Nos. 1 and 2 italics, which can be used effectively in repro-typing; as they have the same unit widths as the Roman characters, words set on the italic machine can be cut out and will fit perfectly over the Roman, but of course this means two typings and some scissors-and-paste work. Alternatively there are substitutes for italic such as letterspacing, underlining or bold (produced by use of methods described above).

CHAPTER III

LETTERING DEVICES

Hand Drawing and Adhesive Transfers

When characters are needed which are outside the scope of type-writing equipment available, one may have to resort to hand drawing. Nowadays this method can be speeded up by the use of adhesive transfer systems of which there is a wide variety. Letraset, Alfaset, Artype, Chart-Pak, Fingerprint, Presletta, Jet-Set, and Blick Dry Print, are some of the familiar names in this field. They are available in a wide range of type faces and sizes, special characters and symbols, and there is hardly any limit to the special printings which can be ordered providing the quantity is economic. Standard ranges of characters and symbols are available in sheet, strip or roll form.

Basically the adhesive transfer is an accurately formed letter or symbol adhering to the back of a translucent support. By applying pressure to the top of the support, the character can be transferred to the surface of another material. Under all normal conditions these types of lettering will adhere to virtually any paper or board surface and some grades have been formulated to adhere firmly enough for use on drawings which are regularly passed through dyeline machines for print making.

It is also possible to use some transfers on direct image offset litho masters but this practice is not universally successful. Much depends upon operator skill, nature of master surface and length of run required.

Photolettering Equipment

Photolettering equipment generally consists of an enlarger or contact printer in combination with a device which accepts and controls a disc or strip bearing symbols to be copied, so that each symbol is accurately positioned on the copying material.

It is a comparatively slow process and cannot be considered suitable for setting bodytype which can be handled much more expeditiously on a keyboard machine such as an electric typewriter. Photo typesetters are a higher class of equipment outside the scope of our subject.

However, for the setting of display type the photolettering machine has some definite advantages over adhesive lettering, especially when the quantity of such work is large. On some lettering machines, up to 30 or more characters per minute can be set.

Of the two types of machine, the projector type is the more versatile because variation of type size can be achieved from one master disc. With the contact type, on which each letter is reproduced size for size, a separate master is required for each type size as well as for each style. Master strips or discs are normally supplied in printer's point sizes.

Facilities for development of the output of film, which may be negative or positive, vary from one model of machine to another but, using conventional photographic materials, they can always be developed in the usual way in a dark room.

When considering the cost of a photolettering machine one must also take into account the cost of masters for all the founts likely to be required. This can in some cases, be a high extra cost over and above the actual machine cost. The following is a representative selection of machines currently available.

Headliner from Varityper

There are several models of the Headliner, all of the contact printing type using laminated plastic discs as typemasters. The copy medium is 35 mm film or paper on all but the Model 880.

Model 80 is capable of producing display copy in daylight conditions in a wide variety of styles and sizes from 10 to 84 point characters. Characters can be exposed at 40 per minute and the machine can justify either by word or letter spacing. Up to 10 ft of copy can be exposed at a time and it is contained in a lightproof spool for transit to the Model 85, three bath, sprocket driven developing unit. Finished copy is ready for paste-up in 90 seconds. Alternatively, the material can be dish developed.

Model 820 is a self contained daylight display composing unit for office or print room. Improvements include an automatic exposure control, quicker interchangeability of typemasters and improved control panel. The machine incorporates its own fully automatic darkroom unit capable of processing 35 mm film, stripping film and bromide paper.

The model 860 has multiple line capacity—several as well as single lines can be composed on the same 35 mm film or paper.

Model 880 is a compact unit providing means to produce display size copy from 6 to 84 point on bromide paper or film 8½ in. wide up to 25 ft long. Features include automatic proportional letter and word spacing, also exposure timing. Ultra violet light source eliminates the need for dark room working. Carriage return is automatic and operating speed is not less than 30 characters per minute. Offered with this machine is the Model 885 processor which provides drip-dry copy for paste-up in seconds. Alternatively, one can dish develop either film or paper.

Filmotype from Colyer & Southey Ltd.

A contact printing machine using masters in the form of film strip. A very compact machine occupying only 18 square inches of desk space and an automatic processor is available as an extra. The master film is reeled from left to right and exposure of each required character is made as it appears in the view area. Many styles of type in 12 to 144 point sizes are available and it is claimed that up to 20 founts may be in the machine at one time.

Foto-riter from J. J. Huber Ltd.

This contact printing unit has more than 50 type styles from 8 point to 72 point. Individual film slide units are used for each character. Copy can be set exactly as a printer does, with letter spacing, justifying, cutting in, etc., as desired. The dial operated letter spacing mechanism is based on the point system, with 72 spaces on the dial face, each space representing one printer's point. One complete revolution of the dial gives a movement of 72 points, approximately equal to one inch.

Each font comes in loose-leaf pocketed pages which can be stored in a three-ring binder. Composed type is on 35 mm photo paper or film.

Protype from Linotype & Machinery Ltd.

Another contact printing system using a series of flexible strips as masters in a very extensive range of faces available from 6 point to 90 point. The type of sensitised material used enables all stages to be carried out in normal office lighting conditions. Exposure time is 2 seconds, developing 30 to 60 seconds, 2 minutes fixing, and 5 min-

(*Top left*) Starsettograph Projection type Photosetter

(*Top right*) Varityper Headliner Model 80

(*Middle left*) Varityper Headliner Model 820

(*Middle right*) Filmotype

(*Bottom*) Foto-Riter Deluxe Model 325

SOME EXAMPLES
OF PHOTOLETTERING EQUIPMENT

utes drying. The working surface on the machine will accommodate
sheets of sensitised material (paper or film) up to 17 in. wide and
12 in. deep but larger sheets can be used by sliding in either direction
under the carriage guides. Speed of operation is approximately
12 characters per minute. Spacing and justification are semi-automatic. The inclined working surface is back-lighted and the full
visible control of the system at all stages enables the most complex
settings to be undertaken without difficulty.

Starsettograph from J. J. Huber Ltd.

This is a projection model using one master plate for all face sizes.
More than 270 typefaces are available which can be printed in continuous sizes from $\frac{3}{32}$ in. to 4 in. Positive right or reverse reading
copy can be produced and screened, superimposed, distorted and
other effects are possible. The positioning of characters is made in
red light and exposure is then 1 to 6 seconds in white light. Characters
go immediately black. Operation can be carried out in yellow light
for convenience in reading manuscript if a different composing
material is used.

There is an electronic exposure timer and fine adjustment device
for positioning lines.

Letterphot from Stephenson Blake & Co. Ltd.

Another projection type setting copy from 6 point up to 4 in.;
variation being made from a single disc by moving the projector head
up and down. Any normal photographic material may be used up to
a maximum of $17\frac{1}{4}$ in. by $4\frac{7}{8}$ in. Light intensity and exposure time
are calculated from calibrations on the supporting column. Once
calculated for given conditions, exposure control is automatic.

Standard justification is achieved by a visual bar below each letter
which is screened when exposure is made. Another device enables a
trial run to be made on luminous foil before proceeding with actual
copy. An extensive range of popular typefaces is available.

Typro from Friden Ltd.

A photocomposing machine offered as a perfect adjunct to the
Justowriter when versatility is required in typesetting. Two options
are available, one a desk top model with portable dark room, the
other in cabinet form with automatic development. Typro operates
in normal light, offers a choice of 1800 type founts from 6 to 144

point and requires no special knowledge of typography or photography. It carries up to 15 founts on one master reel and allows automatic switching of founts. It can compose directly on paper or film; print more than one line on a single strip; make reverses directly; centre or justify copy.

Strip Printer from Krisson Printing Ltd.

A small display contact printer of basically simple construction with a wide choice of typefaces, 6 to 96 point. Type is produced on film or paper carried on 35 mm reels. Master strips are moved through the machine exposing individual characters as selected. Visual spacing is applied by means of a scale on the edge of each fount. The photo paper has a slow emulsion and subdued light is suitable for operations with a red-tinted lamp illuminating the exposure area. Amber jars are provided for processing but an automatic processor is available.

Photonymograph from Barr & Stroud Ltd.

Another projection type machine of considerable versatility. Standard discs are circular glass plates carrying 285 negative characters arranged in three concentric circles and normally carrying three alphabets. Fifteen typefaces are available but others can be made specially. Type size range is nominally $3\frac{1}{2}$ to 36 point. Two interchangeable lettering heads are available; one taking paper or film up to 6 in. wide for tabulated column work with right hand justifier; another for titling or captions takes 35 mm paper or film.

This machine is power operated for film carriage, register or exposure and has an average speed of 1200 characters per hour. It is a large machine having a gross weight of $2\frac{3}{4}$ cwt.

CHAPTER IV

OFFICE COMPOSING MACHINES

Although most electric typewriters will provide a high quality of typescript with the constant even impression necessary in the preparation of master copy for reproduction processes, there are three typographic features which distinguish the normal typewriter from the so called "composing machine".

These distinguishing features are, the capability of proportional spacing of character, automatic alignment of the right hand margin and versatility in the changing of type sizes, faces and line spacings.

There are several of the otherwise conventional electric machines which have the proportional spacing feature, amongst these are the Hermes "Ambassador", the I.B.M. "Executive" and Olivetti "Raphael" and "Editor". Of these the "Executive" is by far the more widely used. It has a much wider range of typefaces and also a rather valuable facility of interchangeable typebars.

Machines having the right hand margin justification feature are the Justowriter, the Varityper, the Olivetti "Editor", the Executive and the I.B.M. 72 Composers.

The field narrows when rapid interchangeability of type faces is considered, to the Varitypers and the I.B.M. 72 Machines.

The choice of machine depends on circumstances and requirements of the work to be performed. Proportional spacing, line justification and variable type faces may not always be necessary. For most people the initial issue is probably cost but even so, typographic considerations cannot be ignored and it is extremely important to be sure that the requirements are clearly worked out. The following information is intended to assist in this direction.

Proportional Spacing

This is probably the most desirable feature for typewriter composition. It provides the elegance necessary for prestige correspondence and the close simulation of letterpress printing needed in any kind of book or brochure.

fixed-width	variable-width
iiii	iiii
oooo	oooo
wwww	wwww
mmmm	mmmm
MMMM	MMMM
WWWW	WWWW
OOOO	OOOO
JJJJ	JJJJ
IIII	IIII

iiiiii
eeeeeee
mmmmmm
IIIIII
EEEEEE
MMMMMM

I.B.M. Executive   Olivetti Editor

STANDARD SPACING	PROPORTIONAL SPACING	UNIT WIDTH
iiii	iiii	2 units
oooo	oooo	3 units
wwww	wwww	4 units
mmmm	mmmm	5 units

Standard Spacing

Vertical lines are formed by the white spaces between the rows of characters as shown by the ruled lines.

Proportional Spacing

In the proportionally typed page there are no vertical lines to distract the eye of the reader.

Friden Justowriter

PROPORTIONAL SPACING

How three manufacturers (IBM, Olivetti and Justowriter) demonstrate the principles of proportional spacing.

The IBM Executive and Friden Justowriter work on a 5-unit system, all characters being allocated one of four widths: 2, 3, 4 or 5 units. There are no one-unit characters, but alphanumeric codes and spacing controls cover all five widths between them. Spacing controls on the Executive are:

2-unit forward (standard word space)

3-unit forward (fitted with repeater action (typamatic); useful for figure work since all figures and comma are 3-unit).

1-unit back.

1-unit 'expand' (for adding one unit to each keytap automatically.)

To move 1-unit forward requires two taps: 2-unit forward and 1-unit back. Tabulating stops are at 4-unit intervals (The Justowriter has no 'expand' key, but there is a 1-unit forward code).

The Varityper 720 works on a 4-unit system, all characters being allocated one of three widths: 2, 3 or 4-units. Standard word spacing is 3-units. The Hermes Ambassador also has a 4-unit system.

The Olivetti Raphael has 3-unit widths of $\frac{1}{2}$, 1 and $1\frac{1}{2}$, 1 being taken as the standard, and characters are allocated to all of these. The Editor, like the Executive, uses a 5-unit system with four groups of character widths. Single units of space are for backspacing and an 'expand' lever adds one space unit between each letter and each word.

The unit spacing allocated to each character will obviously vary according to system but generally most capitals and lower case m and w are one size larger than the majority of lower case. Capital I and J are narrower than other capitals and lower f, i, l and t are on the narrowest width. In the higher unit system the greatest width will, of course, be used for the capital M and W.

The actual width of each unit will depend upon the type size used. The Executive has three pitches of 1/32, 1/36, and 1/45 inch per unit. Justowriter is the same except that their smallest pitch is 1/48 in. and they relate their type sizes to printers' points and so offer five point sizes within the three pitches: 8, 10, 11, 12 and 14 pt.

Similarly Varityper offer a complete range of point sizes but all grouped within four pitches which they call 'scales' A, B, C and D. However, a new Varityper, Model 565, with 5-unit spacing, has recently been announced. It will accommodate a range of type sizes from 4 pt to 13 pt within five 'scales' B, C, D, E and F.

The most recent proportional spacing machine is the IBM 72 Composer in which a nine-unit system means that the letters or symbols on an 88 character type head may vary in width from three to nine units.

Justifying of Right Hand Margin

There are three methods of aligning the right hand margin: those used on the Justowriter, on the Varityper and on all other machines (manual and electric). Basically all involve a second typing and the principle is the same in each case. The amount of space by which the end of each line of typing and the pre-determined right hand margin differ on the first typing is, on the second, distributed (by adding or subtracting) over the spaces between words.

On the Justowriter and MT 72 Composer, the retyping is done automatically. On the Varityper and IBM 72 Composer, the retyping is carried out manually but word spacing is adjusted automatically. On the Olivetti Editor the first typing of each line does not produce copy but is done only to indicate line length for calculating the necessary adjustment and, when this is arrived at, the second typing follows on line by line to give justified copy.

The manual method for all other machines involves straightforward typing of first copy, calculating adjustments in line lengths

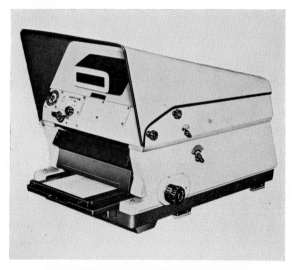

THE OPTYPE COMPOSING MACHINE

and retyping with required word space adjustments. The machines providing differential spacing offer some advantage over fixed width ones in minimising the variation in word spacing.

The 5-unit system is the best in this respect since it allows fractional adjustments in spacing to be made.

There is one other method of achieving justified margins by using additional equipment to the typewriter in the form of photographic units which optically condense or expand lines of unjustified type to a common length. Two makes of equipment working on the same general principles are known as Optype and Flash-o-Line.

On the following page an original copy typed on an IBM Executive, fitted with Bold Face type, is reproduced at two-thirds of original size via a conventional process camera. Following this is a specimen reduced size reproduction made from the same original, but employing the Optype optical justifying machine at the reduction stage. It illustrates the various composing facilities of this versatile piece of equipment.

Varityper

The Varityper is a machine which is well established in the field of reprotyping. It sets a very high standard in quality of copy and the more highly automated tape-controlled machines compete by virtue of higher output potential rather than quality of copy. The other machines with reprotyping capability are basically normal electric typewriters with extended facilities which make them suitable for typewriter composition at an economic figure.

The Varityper Corporation prefer to call their machine an office composing machine, and only in the trade name of Varityper do they acknowledge its relationship to a typewriter. However, in that it is a direct impression machine, we can properly call it a typewriter despite its many odd-man-out characteristics. The most obvious of these is, of course, the interchangeable type founts, two of which can be accommodated on the machine at one time. Another is the back-strike action of a hammer against the type fount instead of the front-strike of a typebar against a platen.

The founts are curved metal alloy segments, and it is the great variety of type styles and sizes available in this form which makes the Varityper so outstanding in the field of type composition. It takes less than a second to change type founts and as two are in use at one time, matching italics, bold face or special symbols can be inserted in the copy as typing proceeds. Instantly variable spacing to match the individual type size and style of each font is another feature of the machine.

The keyboard is arranged in only three banks of keys instead of the usual four. There are, therefore, two shift positions. There are a number of Varityper models designed for different applications, some of which have a different keyboard arrangement and not all have the automatic margin justifying or proportional spacing facilities. For example the model 350 is an engineering lettering machine with a very long carriage suitable for typing information on drawings, bills of material and similar large technical documents, which do not require these features.

In our present context we are only concerned with the models giving the maximum facilities for reprotyping which we find in the model 720 and the new 565.

Although it is necessary to type twice to achieve justified copy on the Varityper the word spacing is adjusted automatically and is regular throughout the justified version. This is a unique feature. The first typing has to finish within a 'justification area' near the end of the line, as indicated on the dial on the machine. This is adjusted prior to the second typing, each word space having been automatically calculated by a special device which then unwinds so that the spaces fill the line out evenly (to a maximum of 15 spaces).

Line spacing can be varied within a wide range of precalibrated selections from $\frac{1}{2}$ point to 18 points with the precision of professional typography. The operator simply selects the desired spacing and the line advance lever inserts the spacing between lines automatically.

Forms, of even a highly complex nature, can be ruled and type composed in the very same operation. Any style of line or leader can be ruled automatically and with a very high degree of precision. The operator simply inserts the type font bearing the desired type style and ruling or leader segment, and depresses the 'rule' button. The rest is automatic. A micro-sharp line or leader will appear on the page to the exact length desired. The text is then typed in as ruling progresses.

The one-time carbon ribbon is standard on Varitypers and in the case of the model 720 the ribbon is automatically rewound within the machine for clean and convenient disposal.

The Varityper uses its electrical power in a somewhat different manner to other machines. The carriage action is manual, but the type striking action, of the hammer against the face of the type font, is controlled by an electrically wound spring motor box.

Optype is a composing and optical justifying machine which will
take the original typed manuscript and square up the right hand margin.
It obtains this result simply by photographing each individual line, which
is optically "moved" when it is projected through a lens so that it is either
compressed or expanded. The physical appearance of the characters   xx 1
remains unaltered, as justification of the line is spread evenly and in
proportion over its entire length.

Optype has many other versatile features. For example, the machine
will optically reduce the size of the type, if required, by up to 25% in a
single operation. A further reduction of the resulting negative can give
an ultimate total reduction of up to 44%.

With Optype the height of the letters can also be increased by 12%
without their width being affected in any way.

Yet another optical device enables Optype to turn the original text
into italics;these can likewise be increased in height. A word, or words,
within a line can even be'boldened"   x
within a line can even be "boldened". Furthermore, all the operations
mentioned here can be conbined, thus making possible a wide selection   xx2
of style variations from a single typed manuscript.

With a little practice and experiment, Optype has many specialised
uses in the speedy and economical reproduction of technical matter involving symbols, for example, and for cartography, tabulating, and other
intricate and normally costly composing work.

Different column widths present no problem as Optype is able to
produce to newspaper, magazine and book formats. Similarly, screened
negatives can be produced from original photographs. These and line
drawings can be introduced by Optype into the make-up.

Because Optype operates on a line-by-line basis it is easy to correct
a typing error at the outset, thus eliminating proof reading at a later,
more costly stage. The typist merely leaves the faulty line and retypes
it correctly either immediately below, or at the foot of the sheet. The
marginal indications on this page are the simple code she follows to show
exactly where a revised line should be inserted when it is being putthrough   x
exactly where a revised line should be inserted when it is being put through
Optype.

Operating speeds are astonishingly high. Using ortho film, each   x
Operating speeds are astonishingly high. Using an ortho film, each
line requires exposure for only 3 seconds — the page you are now reading
was processed by Optype in $3\frac{1}{2}$ minutes.

Optype is entirely in step with present and future trends in photo
composition for offset printing.

compressed or expanded. The physical appearance of the characters   xx1

mentioned here can be combined, thus making possible a wide selection   xx2

ORIGINAL MANUSCRIPT STYLE

This page reproduces an original manuscript typed on an
IBM Executive machine fitted with Bold Face type.

JUSTIFICATION AND STYLE VARIATION (*opposite*)

Reproduction with photographically justified margin plus
several style variations, all by the Optype system.

Optype is a composing and optical justifying machine which will take the original typed manuscript and square up the right hand margin. It obtains this result simply by photographing each individual line, which is optically "moved" when it is projected through a lens so that it is either compressed or expanded. The physical appearance of the characters remains unaltered, as justification of the line is spread evenly and in proportion over its entire length. **(i)**

Optype has many other versatile features. For example, the machine will optically reduce the size of the type, if required, by up to 25% in a single operation. A further reduction of the resulting negative can give an ultimate total reduction of up to 44%. **(ii)**

With Optype the height of the letters can also be increased by 12% without their width being affected in any way. **(iii)**

Yet another optical device enables Optype to turn the original text into italics; these can likewise be increased in height. A word, or words, within a line can even be "boldened". Furthermore, all the operations mentioned here can be combined, thus making possible a wide selection of style variations from a single typed manuscript. **(iv)**

With a little practice and experiment, Optype has many specialised uses in the speedy and economical reproduction of technical matter involving symbols, for example, and for cartography, tabulating, and other intricate and normally costly composing work. **(v)**

Different column widths present no problem as Optype is able to produce to newspaper, magazine and book formats. Similarly, screened negatives can be produced from original photographs. These and line drawings can be introduced by Optype into the make-up. **(vi)**

Because *Optype* operates on a line-by-line basis it is easy to correct a typing error at the outset, thus eliminating proof reading at a later, more costly stage. The typist merely leaves the faulty line and retypes it correctly either immediately below, or at the foot of the sheet. The marginal indications on this page are the *simple* code she follows to show exactly where a revised line should be inserted when it is being put through Optype. **(vii)**

Operating speeds are astonishingly high. Using an ortho film, each line requires exposure for only *3 seconds* — the page you are now reading was processed by Optype in $3\frac{1}{2}$ minutes. **(viii)**

Optype is entirely in step with present and future trends in photo composition for offset printing. **(ix)**

Paragraph (ii) is italicised throughout
Paragraph (iv) is condensed throughout
Paragraph (v) is italicised and condensed
Paragraph (vii) italicises or condenses one or more words
Paragraph (viii) italicises and condenses one or more words

It should be observed that by a second operation OPTYPE will reduce the negative to give an ultimate total reduction of up to 44% of the original text. This page shows the result thus obtained

On this second reduction, furthermore, a word or words may actually be "boldened" as indicated in paragraph (ix)

(*Top left*) Varityper Model 720

(*Middle left*) IBM Executive 'D'

(*Bottom left*) Imperial Dual Unit 458

(*Top right*) IBM 72

(*Middle right*) Olivetti Editor

(*Bottom right*) IBM 72 Composer

MACHINES WITH SPECIAL FACILITIES FOR TYPEWRITER
COMPOSITION

However the Varityper is not without disadvantages, the principle one being that it is heavy in action and slow in operation. On this account some prefer to forego extensive variability of typeface and choose one of the tape controlled writing machines because of the higher output capacity.

IBM 72 Typewriter

Although the IBM 72 looks like an ordinary typewriter, it incorporates radically different design features and the most important of these is the single-element typing head. This is a small metal ball containing all 88 characters found in an ordinary typewriter and it replaces conventional typebars. This ball spins and tilts to strike the

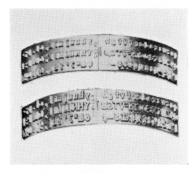

VARITYPER TYPE FOUNT

Two founts are in use at one time and additional founts are inserted in the machine in a second or two.

IBM 72 PRINTING HEAD

Smaller than a golf ball and interchangeable for changing type styles in seconds.

paper with the right character at the touch of a key. No moving carriage is required as the head itself moves across the sheet as the typing proceeds. The absence of carriage movement eliminates vibration and makes the machine quiet in use. A built-in stroke storage system enables the machine to remember the order in which the keys are struck and when two keys are struck too quickly the machine delays action on the second letter until the first has been printed.

To the reprographer, another important feature of the 72 is the interchangeability of the typing head enabling type styles to be changed in a matter of seconds.

Refinements which are included on the 72 are five typamatic keys – space-bar, carrier return and line-space, back-space, hyphen/underscore and vertical index. These keys, when depressed and held, repeat their particular operations at speed. Reverse tabulation enables tabulating to be done in both directions. By using the vertical index key and tab-key together with other typamatic keys, access to any point on the paper is quick and accurate. The ease of ribbon changing is another attractive feature; it is housed in a removable cartridge which can be changed in seconds without soiling the hands.

The IBM 71 is identical to the 72 but is equipped to take a plastic film ribbon for the typing of offset litho masters. The facility to vary the force with which the typehead strikes the plate is provided. This is an important feature in view of the variety of thicknesses encountered with paper masters.

IBM 72 Composer

Based on the IBM 72 typewriter, IBM have introduced two composing machines which compete strongly with the Varityper and Justowriter systems. The IBM 72 Composer is a semi-automatic machine and the IBM MT 72 Composer is fully automatic.

The advantages of the interchangeable golf-ball head are well employed in both machines. There are more than 50 type founts available for the two machines in five type families, Press Roman, Aldine Roman, Bodoni Book, Pyramid and Univers. All are in a variety of weights, styles and sizes. There are 46 text type faces in all, and others are for mathematical and technical symbols plus other languages.

In addition to the features offered by the model 72 electric typewriter, the 72 Composer incorporates a nine-unit proportional spacing system and semi-automatic line justification. There is also a leading-out facility ranging from 5 point to 20 point, which is dial set and fully automatic. A typing speed of 14 characters per second is possible with a character back-space memory which remembers the last six to nine characters. Sharp, well defined images are achieved with a one-time carbon ribbon. Margins may be justified either right or left of centre but a typist skilled in composition work is necessary to make the best use of all the machine facilities available. Interword spacing, line length, depth of paragraph indentation, are all matters for operator decision.

A dual purpose typamatic index key feeds the paper forward into the machine continuously, or in one line steps, to the typing position. A leading dial gives any required line spacing from 5 to 20 points. The escapement mechanism is adjusted according to the point size of the typing head in use by matching a three-colour control to the colour code of the typing head.

A no-print key is provided to enable lines to be pre-measured before centring or ranging copy on the right. The standard method of preparing justified copy is to prepare a draft first. The first line is typed, after setting the justification tube, and terminated at the end of a word or syllable, just inside the right hand margin. The reading in the justification window, which is in the form of a colour code and a number, is then typed at the end of the line. This continues line by line. In retyping the final copy, or duplicating master, justified copy is automatically produced by setting the justification dial to the colour and number recorded on the draft for each line.

When justified copy of only around six inches width is required, the draft and finished copy can be produced side by side on the same sheet. The justification dial can then be set line by line directly from the reading in the justification window.

IBM MT 72 Composer

The MT 72 Composer is entirely automatic and employs magnetic tape on which to store the manually typed information. A tape reader and associated console provide the output device which automatically produces the justified copy. Errors are dealt with by back-spacing and retyping at the stage of producing the initial proof copy and tape. More extensive alterations can be put on a second control tape and merged with the master tape (see page 67).

The operator-controlled composer panel links the reader unit to a modified 72 Composer, which carries out any format instruction with minimum operator intervention.

The MT 72 Composer features two distinct and separate functions of automatic type-setting, the Magnetic Tape Recorder for key-boarding original source material and the Tape Composer Console with solid state logic Magnetic Tape Reader (two stations) operating a modified 72 Composer.

The MT 72 Recorder has the following features. It produces hard copy for proof reading; has one magnetic tape station for recording only and no playback capability; encode reference code for searching; backspace and strikeover for corrections on hard copy and magnetic media; line return for correcting copy and tape; 100 feet of tape in cartridge to store approximately 24,000 characters and spaces.

The MT Composer Console consists of two free standing units. The two station Magnetic Tape Reader reads tape at approximately

20 characters per second; searches the magnetic tape at 900 characters per second and merges tape for correction procedures; re-reads characters for parity error checks.

The Composer Control is a desk housing core memory and solid state logic. This unit automatically performs the following composition functions. Prepares body text in required justified and leadered format in line measure up to approximately 9 inches. Operator choice may control many variables such as interword spacing, line length to fine limits, paragraph and line indentation, etc.

IBM Executive

The Executive, ostensibly an electric typewriter for prestige correspondence, is also an ideal machine for preparing top quality masters for reproduction processes and it is very widely used for this purpose. It is cheap in comparison with the specialist composing machines and its 5-unit proportional spacing gives such a high quality of typescript that its popularity in this field is not surprising.

The Executive also has the facility of specially designed changeable typebars. These can extend the range of a selected font by eight to a dozen extra characters if they are needed. A very wide range of typeface is available and also of additional characters. Because it is such a widely used machine, a number of attachments have been developed to still further extend its scope, such as the 'Alphamod' and boldening devices described in Chapter II.

The Executive 'D' is a new model incorporating several improvements on the superseded model in the 'C' range. It is certainly quieter in operation and has seven typamatic keys, a space-bar expand control, Centre Point Scale and a No Print mechanism to simplify right hand margin justifying.

The machine has many other features to assist in the production of perfect typescript with a beautifully even but crisp impression regardless of who does the typing.

Olivetti Editor

The Olivetti Editor electric typewriter is a machine offering a five-unit proportional spacing feature and an automatic right-hand-margin justifying facility. A polyethylene carbon ribbon, automatic impact control for capitals and an overall three-positional impact control, provide an elegance of impression well suited to the task of reprotyping. Type faces available are designed to exploit the full

50

potentialities of proportional spacing but, like the IBM Executive, once the preferred type face is chosen there is no built-in interchangeability of type face.

However, Uneoprint Technical Aids have already produced a modified version of their Alphamod attachment to suit the Editor machine and this enables an extensive range of additional characters to be included in the text during normal typing. These attachments are described in Chapter II.

The method of obtaining a justified right hand margin on the Editor is interesting and practical. It involves double typing but no unjustified copy is produced, only the finished justified version. While the document itself is in the machine, the operator types the first line then, before actually typing the next, presses a button and goes on typing normally. But the keys do not strike the paper. When the end of the line is reached, a movable scale indicates the number of spaces to be lost or gained between words to make the line the same width as the preceding one. The operator acts upon the information as the line is retyped, this time as hard copy on the document. To make measurement easier the space bar has two parts, one giving two spacing units; the other three, and for maximum accuracy the backspace key moves the carriage through one spacing unit only.

An automatic expander, controlled by a lever, adds one basic space unit between each letter and each word.

Key down	**EDITOR**
Key up	**E D I T O R**
Key down + 2 unit space bar	**E D I T O R**
Key down + 3 unit space bar	**E D I T O R**
Key up + 2 unit space bar	**E D I T O R**
Key up + 3 unit space bar	**E D I T O R**

EXPANDED WRITING

Express margin-setting is another special feature of the Editor. A single express margin-setting key allows two left hand margins to be set simultaneously, with instant change between each margin. This is useful for layout purposes. For example, a quotation or a paragraph may be emphasised by indenting each line and then returning to the normal left hand margin. The same key also controls reverse tabulation.

51

Hermes Ambassador

The Ambassador is another electric machine which is useful for reprotyping due to its 4-unit proportional spacing feature. It is equipped with double spirit carbon and fabric ribbon attachments and there is a choice of several typefaces. It has 46 keys, variable type pressure, automatic tabulator, repetition key for each of 92 characters and automatic line spacing.

CHAPTER V

AUTOMATIC WRITING MACHINES

Typewriters linked to a mechanism specially designed or adapted to produce a key punched paper record which, in turn, can be used to reproduce a document automatically, were originally intended to produce letters having the appearance of being personally typed for each recipient.

These machines are operated by a large perforated roll of paper, paper tape or, more recently, magnetic tape. Both the roll and the tape may contain many paragraphs or complete letters which may be of any length. A special selection device fitted on the machine enables any letter to be punched automatically or paragraphs may be preselected and typed in any given order. The machine can also be made to stop at any required position allowing additional information to be added as indicated by the selector.

Although prepared automatically the copy is, in fact, a typed letter, so that if the name and address of the recipient is added the result is indistinguishable from a letter which has been individually typed.

As an indication of the output possible by these automatic typewriter machines it is claimed that one girl can produce 110–120 letters per day, or approximately 24,000 words, when fairly standardised forms of letters are required. Used in this way, automatic typing is a reprographic process in itself. It is about three times more expensive for a standard letter than printing by offset-litho and addressing each in turn but, for the extra expense, the automatic typewriter provides original and individual letters and, to the recipient, there is nothing to indicate that anyone else has received a similar communication.

Automatic typewriters have many economic applications other than letter writing and are particularly useful for the composition of reports, specifications, instruction manuals, price lists, and telephone directories when several stages of drafting are often unavoidable. The facility for rapid correction and insertion of additions without manually retyping the approved portions, saves checking as well as typing time. In addition tapes may be stored, indexed and withdrawn from file for further reproduction of copy of any required portion of composition recorded.

Wide Paper Tape or Roll Operated Machines

An example of the roll type machine is the Auto-typist Model 6350. Letters or paragraphs are perforated on a wide paper roll, very similar to that used in a player piano. A panel of pushbuttons corresponds to different paragraphs and all the operator has to do is to type the heading and salutation, touch the appropriate pushbuttons and the machine does the rest at a high typing speed – up to 150 words per minute.

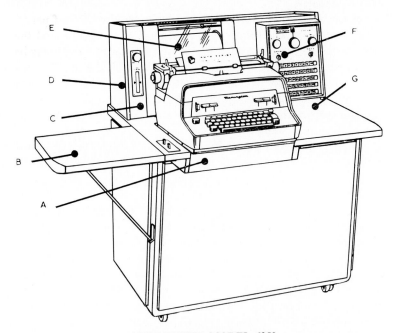

AUTO-TYPIST MODEL 6350

A. Recessed desk well encloses typewriter connection system. B. Extension shelf gives added working area. (optional). C. Built-in correction block simplifies making changes on "memory" tape. D. Built-in line counter—stops automatic typing after a predetermined number of lines have been typed. (optional). E. Record roll clearly visible through Plexiglass window to check selection and tape alignment. F. Control panel offers 50 choices of pre-composed sentences, paragraphs, letters. "Memory" tape stores 300 typewritten lines. G. Large 14″ × 20″ working area to right of typewriter.

A further development of this machine is the Auto-typist 65100 which gives a wider range of selectivity by the employment of dual rolls of memory tape which can store up to 36,000 characters. Pre-selection of paragraphs in any one of hundreds of desired combinations is by manipulation of a 100 pushbutton control panel. The machine can be programmed to stop automatically at any desired point for the insertion of variable or individual copy.

Like other Auto-typist models the 65100 can be used as an output printer in conjunction with most makes of electric typewriter including proportional spacing machines. Output typing speed is limited only by the make and model of the typewriter attached; and this when not being used for automatic typing, can be used manually.

The 65100 employs a design feature known as fluid logic, which requires fewer moving parts than electronic control and has a characteristic of extreme accuracy.

The Auto-typist uses 50-channel, 11 in. wide, paper tape and perforation is carried out on a separate machine. This may be purchased or the perforating can be done by an Auto-typist dealer. One tape can operate several typewriters simultaneously using "slave" auxiliary units. The particular typewriter chosen can be easily interchanged with others of the same model (including proportional spacing machines) permitting the use of different type faces.

The Logabax Supertyper S is another roll type automatic typewriter with a speed claimed to be up to 180 words per minute. It is a very compact model occupying desk space of only 24 in. × 20 in. and, compared with other automatic writing machines, it is in a low price bracket. The superstructure is designed to act as a silencer which reduces noise by 50 per cent.

The Royal McBee Royaltyper is an automatic typing system which produces a code punched paper tape of the wide variety as opposed to the narrow tape of the 5 to 8 channel system discussed in the following section. The Royaltyper consists of a specially designed electric typewriter, a tape reader, a tape punch and a control unit all integrated into a single desk unit. The tape is produced as an automatic by-product of the normal typing function and it can be used to operate the same, or other, Royaltypers automatically at a speed three or four times that of manual typing. Like other machines in this category, it is intended for the production of personalised correspondence containing a fair amount of repetitive text.

The Filetape version of this machine, instead of a long tape on which a number of master documents are recorded and later selected by numbered keys, uses shorter lengths of folded tape. This allows a large library of tapes to be built up which may consist of complete pages or paragraphs. Provision can be made for adding variable information in the body of the document.

Narrow Paper Tape Operated Machines

The typewriter records on tape or edge punched cards the whole or selected parts of a document, simultaneously with the original typing. The tape or cards can subsequently be passed through the reading unit to control the typewriter for the automatic reproduction of the stored information in typed form. Some installations use slave typewriters.

This type of equipment can be usefully employed for the recording and typing of letters of a standard or semi-standard nature, production and purchase orders, specifications, and it is particularly useful in the field of listed information which regularly requires up-dating.

In letter typing, names and addresses can be punched on cards and the text on tape. Codes control the card reader to type the name and address and the tape reader to type the text matter. At the same time, further codes control the punch unit to prepare a by-product tape recording the names and addresses for the typing of envelopes.

Tapes can be coded to stop the typewriter for the manual insertion in a document of variable data. At the same time codes can be used to switch on the punch to record the manual typing.

To facilitate this kind of edited reproduction, additional control features can be incorporated such as word stop and word skip, line stop and line skip, line indent and edit control. The latter allows the alignment of the right hand margin to be controlled regardless of the number of words which are to be inserted or withdrawn.

The life of the electronics of these machines is expected to be at least five years but, owing to the high operating speed, the mechanical parts of the typewriter section are likely to need replacement after two or three years. This fact is usually taken into consideration when maintenance contracts are arranged. Some makers make a special point of strengthening standard typewriters before fitting them to automatic equipment. The typewriter is often inertchangeable with similar models and second machines are sometimes ordered to provide variation of type characters. They cannot be used together but can be changed for different categories of work.

Punched Paper Tape

Punched paper tape is a common language medium for many business machines, electronic computers and data transmission systems. It may have 5, 6, 7 or 8 channels punched in a variety of code patterns. It is more economical and more efficient than punched cards and stores data which can be reproduced at a high speed on an automatic typewriter. Typing and taping is a means of avoiding manual repetitive typing.

Tape produced automatically at the typing stage can be read by a tape reader and printed out on an automatic typewriter at speeds very much higher than can be achieved by manual operation. A tape reader is flexible enough for variable information to be type in manually, and simple enough for most junior typists to supervise efficiently. Manual repetitive typing has already given way to automatic typing in many offices. The increased accuracy is often more important than the enhanced speed—especially where technical or scientific work is involved.

Typing and taping means that you never need type anything more than once.

Paper tape records can be altered or added to very easily. Only the varied data has to be typed again. A new tape, containing the corrected data, and a new copy for checking are produced simultaneously and very quickly.

Tape is punched using a binary code structure and the number of codes it is possible to produce depend on the number of channels accommodated on the tape. There are only two possible code combinations in a single channel: either a hole or no hole. In a 2-channel tape, there are only four possible combinations:

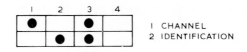

TWO-CHANNEL TAPE

The four possible code combinations in a Two-channel Tape.

In this manner, 3-channel tape has only eight possible code combinations; 4-channel tape has 16 possible code combinations; 5-channel tape, 32; 6-channel tape, 64; and 7-channel tape has 128 possible code combinations.

The first commercially usable punched tape was 5-channel tape, giving 32 possible code combinations. Much of the communications equipment today still uses 5-channel tape.

Most of the automatic punched tape typewriter machines now use 6, 7 or 8 channels and some have a variable facility in this field. When a five channel code is used, of the 32 available codes, 26 would be needed for the alphabet leaving only 6 codes for machine functions. Such machines write capital letters only, and the type basket shifts into upper case (figures) position to write numbers and special characters.

The IBM 8-channel is used as standard on several of the machines described, including the Ultronic 800 on which the eighth channel is used only for the carriage return code.

On the following two pages are examples of seven channel and eight channel code charts.

Tape Operated Typing Machine Features

When comparing the various models of automatic tape input–output writers the purpose and value of the special automatic features have to be studied.

Margin Control automatically returns the carriage to the margin and line feeds when a right hand margin is reached. This right hand margin is set manually and can be varied at will. The left hand margin is variable in the usual manner.

Indent Control automatically returns the carriage to an indent position and line feeds. In some cases a multiple indent control can be an additional facility.

Word Skip operates by pressing a button which causes the tape to be read until the next space is reached, typewriter and output punch being unaffected.

Word Stop is used during typing of a word. The machine stops at the word end, regardless of length of word.

Line Skip is terminated by a carriage return code.

Line Stop is used during typing. The machine stops at next carriage return.

Block Skip is terminated by a deliberately pre-punched end-of-block character.

Edit Control makes it possible to control the alignment of the right hand margin when words are inserted or withdrawn. The actual width of typing line can be narrowed or extended at will, all under automatic control.

Lower Case & Unit Width		Code Position 7654 321	Upper Case & Unit Width	
a	3		A	4
b	3		B	4
c	3		C	4
d	3		D	4
e	3		E	4
f	2		F	4
g	3		G	4
h	3		H	4
i	2		I	2
j	2		J	3
k	3		K	4
l	2		L	4
m	5		M	5
n	3		N	4
o	3		O	4
p	3		P	4
q	3		Q	4
r	3		R	4
s	3		S	3
t	2		T	4
u	3		U	4
v	3		V	4
w	4		W	5
x	3		X	4
y	3		Y	4
z	3		Z	4
1	3		!	2
2	3		@	4
3	3		#	3
4	3		$	3
5	3		%	4
6	3		¢	3
7	3		&	4
8	3		*	3
9	3		(	2
0	3		)	2
-	3		_	3
;	2		:	2
'	2		`	2
,	2		,	2
.	2		.	2
/	3		?	3

Function Codes

Upper Case *
Lower Case *
Back Space *
One Unit *
Three Units *
Space *
Tab
Line Space
Code Delete
Stop Code

Line Delete Code

Justification Code (Basis)

7-CHANNEL FRIDEN
JUSTOWRITER

59

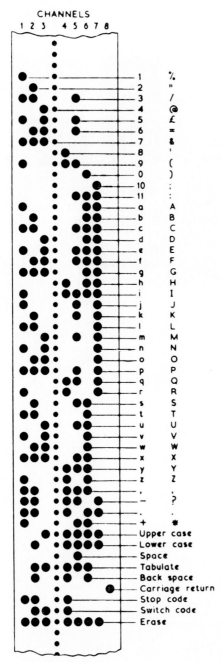

8-CHANNEL ULTRONIC 800/9

60

Edge-Punched Card Facility enables the punch and reader to handle a fanfold or other card with normal code punching down the left hand side.

Tape Back-Up from Typewriter causes the output punch to backfeed by operation of the back space key on the typewriter. This causes the character being altered to be typed over the erased character. The hard copy shows the exact state of the tape.

Type Change provides a number of changeable type bars or even a complete type fount to allow typing of mathematical and engineering symbols.

Code Change for use with either accounting machines or computers is available on all machines but the degree of modification varies.

Carriage Width of 15 in. is considered essential but 17 in. and 20 in. are generally available.

Justowriter System

The Justowriter system is of particular interest to the reprographic man. It is really two machines, one a recorder which produces a proof reading typed copy and a punched paper tape simultaneously. The other is a reproducer or copysetter which operates at 100 words a minute to produce a right hand margin justified master copy ready for reproduction. Corrections and revisions can be made and incorporated in the tape and master copy. The machines are rather expensive but the Justowriter does provide differential spacing of characters and, if different but complementary type styles are chosen for the recorder and reproducer, they can be used together to provide a master in two type faces, giving a still closer resemblance to letterpress printing.

The Model JU Recorder is made up of four major components: the Writing Machine, Code Selector, Computer and Tape Punch.

The Writing Machine: The Writing Machine contains the power supply, the keylevers, and all necessary equipment to allow the Recorder to be used to type a document.

The Code Selector: When the operator touches a keylever, the Code Selector converts the mechanical action of the keylever into a series of electrical impulses, corresponding to the code for that keylever, and sends them to the Tape Punch.

The Computer: The Computer measures the amount of space needed to expand or contract a line to a given length, and sends this measurement, in the form of electrical impulses, to the Tape Punch.

The Tape Punch: If the Tape Punch is on at the time these impulses are received from the Code Selector, a code will be punched into the tape.

The Model AA (Authors Alterations) contains all of the components and features of the Model JU Recorder. In addition, the Model AA has two additional components, a Tape Reader and a Code Translator. These features allow the Model AA the further ability to sense codes in punched tape to cause the Model AA to type automatically. Punched tape can be reproduced, and copy can be revised and altered, while punching a new tape containing the changes. If the tape being "read" in the Tape Reader of the Model AA has been punched on a Motorized Tape Punch attached to a Justowriter Reproducer, the Model AA is capable of producing justified copy automatically.

The Model JU Reproducer is made up of three major components:
The Tape Reader: In the Reproducer this component is a double reader with two reading heads. The back reading head, called the J-Reader, senses those codes originating from the Computer on the Recorder. The front reading head, called the Print Reader, senses textual codes originating from the Code Selector on the Recorder.
The Code Translator: The Code Translator converts these electrical impulses into a mechanical action, causing the keylever on the writing machine, corresponding to that code, to be operated.
The Writing Machine: The Writing Machine contains the power supply, the keylevers, and all necessary equipment to enable the Justowriter to write a document.

Justification on the Justowriter takes place within the first eight word spaces in any line. The normal word space in the recorder is two units but in the reproducer it may be expanded to five units or contracted to one unit. If a line contains at least eight word spaces, that line can be automatically expanded in the reproducer a maximum of 22 units of space, or automatically contracted a maximum of seven units. Any less than eight word spaces decreases the limits of justification.

The computer in the recorder controls the justification in the reproducer. It does three things: counts the number of word spaces in a line, computes how many units of space must be added or subtracted to each word space to justify the line and finally it causes the justifying code to be punched into the tape when the J carriage return is touched. This code is the justifying data to be used by the reproducer.

62

Touching the J carriage return key punches three codes into the tape: the interlock code, the justification code, and the carriage return (line space) code.

The tape reader on the Justowriter reproducer is a double reader. The front reader is called the print reader and the back reader is called the J-reader. Each line in the tape is always fed through the J-reader before feeding through the print reader. Therefore, the justification code is always read before the line is written and will set up the justification spacing for that line.

The interlock code is read by both readers and controls the alternate readings in the double reader. The carriage return code is read

THE JUSTOWRITER JU RECORDER AND REPRODUCER UNITS

only by the print reader, and is considered the first code of the next line. The justification code, having already served its purpose, is ignored by the print reader when read there. All verbage codes are read by the print reader.

Features of other Tape Operated Machines

The Bradma-Dura Mach. 10 is an automatic tape input/output writing machine well suited to letter and report writing as well as many standard office systems. It is a table top machine based on the IBM 72 "golf ball" typewriter. Copy can be reproduced from tape at 15 characters per second via a photo-electric reader and at the same time, it will regenerate tape or edge punch cards. Block, sentence, line and word skip are featured with edit control which automatically adjusts the right hand margin on a second tape when revisions are manually typed in. An automatic ribbon shift is available which records revised data in red.

(*Top left*) Royal Royaltyper

(*Top right*) IBM Magnetic Tape 72

(*Middle left*) Friden 2301 Flexowriter

(*Middle right*) Adrema Dura 1041

(*Bottom*) Ultronic 811

SOME AUTOMATIC WRITING MACHINES

The keyboard is standard but the founts are interchangeable and maximum carriage width is 15 in.

Dura Model 1041. A new automatic typewriter with silicon solid state circuitry. It processes business data, types automatically and produces paper tape for direct computer input in any code. Automatic typing is performed at 15.4 codes per second, or approximately 175 words per minute. Total interlocking of the 1041 allows all components of the writing system to operate at their maximum speed. When not being employed as an automatic, the 1041 may be used as a conventional typewriter. Interchangeable typing heads permit a variety of type styles to be used as required. Character skip or non-print may be controlled manually and the visible margin and tab setting plus quietness of operation make it a comfortable machine to operate.

The Integrated Data Processing Model 703/CL is a desk mounted machine using an IBM model C Typewriter. Playback from tape is at 12 characters per second from a mechanical reader. Word skip and block skip together with margin control are available.

The Ultronic 811 also uses an IBM model C typewriter. Reading speed is 10 characters per second. Margin control, multiple indent control, word, line and block skip, word and line stop are available facilities. An edit control feature makes it possible to produce edited copy with semi-justified right hand margin. Large or small passages can be inserted during editing and the actual width of typing line can be narrowed or extended at will under automatic control. Tape back up from the typewriter can be supplied if required. Another interesting and useful optional feature is the provision of an underline character on a non-escapement key. This allows typing of the underline and then the character, eliminating the need to backspace normally required for underlining. An auxiliary reader can be fitted if required. Eight channel code is standard.

The Vonamatic (*British Equipment Co. Ltd.*) uses an IBM model C typewriter. Reading speed on a mechanical reader is 10 characters per second with a skip speed of 20 per second. Margin control, word, line and block skip are available and tape back up from the typewriter can be fitted. Edge punched cards can be handled and auxiliary readers and punches can be fitted. This machine also has the automatic ribbon colour change as previously described. All 5, 6, 7 or 8 channel coding systems can be supplied, 8 channel being the standard. A facility is available for incorporating two codes switching from one to the other as required.

The Logabax Supertyper Selectograph and Advocate are recent additions to the range of tape-operated machines. Both employ IBM 72 typewriters. The Selectograph incorporates its own punch-perforator and reader. A print out speed of 180 words a minute is backed up by a skip speed of 300 codes per second.

The machine can be programmed to select any required information from a master tape. An edge punch card reader can be linked to allow variable information such as names and addresses, part numbers, etc., to be inserted as required. Further automation can be introduced to accommodate continuous stationery and alternatively needle-hole selection cards to select appropriate data for print out. An additional tape reader, instead of a card reader, can be fitted and a line counter supplied if required.

The Advocate is a machine which automatically deletes any part of the draft copy and allows any additional text to be typed in regardless of the length of deletion or substitution. By use of the edit control unit the machine automatically justifies the remaining text to give uniformity. Print out speed and skip speed are as for the Selectograph.

The Friden "Flexowriter" is an automatic writing machine with a paper tape output which can be stored and used for repeat typing on the same machine. It is widely used in office systems work in the preparation of standard paper work with variable features. Alternatively edge punch cards or tabulating cards can be used as input and output and a wide range of auxiliary input/output units may be cable connected to form a complete data processing system.

In cases where there is a need to continually retype office duplicating masters, a "Flexowriter" can be employed to save much of the copytyping labour.

The Friden "President" model is ideal for all repetitive writing applications, with proportional spacing ensuring high quality appearance. The machine has many programming facilities which make it very efficient and simple to operate. All carriage movement is controlled by the programme.

Other models are also available for special applications, one using the special characters and magnetic ink employed in banking applications.

A new introduction from Friden's is the 2300 Series of Flexowriters. Drawing on their considerable experience of customers' systems requirements, they have been able to 'tailor-make' a range of new machines, each of which is designed for a specific type of application. The series is backed by a full range of auxiliary equipment, such as data selectors, readers, punches and converters.

The simplest machine in the series, the 2303NC, is intended solely for numerical control work. Other machines cope with repetitive letter writing, offset litho work, basic systems tasks using punched tape or cards and computer oriented tasks such as programme editing and systems applications to a specific computer. The most sophisticated model in the series is the 2301.

Magnetic Tape Writing Machine

Another development in the field of automatic typewriting is the IBM magnetic tape writing machine. Instead of on paper tape, the typed information is stored on magnetic tape which is immediately available for retyping at 15 characters per second. Copy changes can be made manually as automatic retyping is halted at the appropriate point. Since the retyping can be stopped at a single character, word end or line end, the correction is carried out quickly and simply.

As the correction is typed it is recorded on the second tape. The result is a correct modified tape and a correction-free typewritten master copy. Line lengths are adjusted automatically when margins have been changed manually. If copy is added or deleted, sentences and paragraphs are re-spaced electronically and accurately.

During typing, coding can be recorded on the tape to facilitate search for selected copy for retyping. A simple turn of a reference number switch and a touch of the search key are the only operations necessary to instruct the machine to scan at 900 characters per second, locate and combine information stored on the cartridges at the two tape stations for retyping. The retyping page of excerpts from reports is thus made very easy.

Each tape cartridge can hold 24,000 characters, approximately 6 pages of closely typed foolscap. Recordings on the tapes can be erased quickly when they are no longer required and the tape used time and time again.

Several models of the IBM Magnetic Tape 72 Typewriter are available. Model I and Model II have a single recording and playback station; Model II can record, select and locate up to 80 reference codes on magnetic tape and, if necessary, automatically adjust right hand margins. Model III and Model IV have two recording and playback stations; can transfer recorded material from one tape to another and merge material on both tapes into one typewritten result. In addition Model IV will accept variable length insertions from one tape to the other while typing out recorded material and record, select and locate up to 80 reference codes on magnetic tape.

CHAPTER VI

TYPEWRITER RIBBONS AND CARBONS

The standard ribbons used for typing of normal correspondence are usually on fabric base and are retained on the machine until the typed image deteriorates. Black and a variety of colours are available; also two colours on one ribbon. This long life depends upon the capillary action of the ink recharging used portions from the unused portions of the ribbon so that it can be reversed from spool to spool across the machine until either ink or fabric gives out.

Fabric Ribbon

Most fabric ribbons are made from Egyptian cotton. The weaving of the yarn demands a high standard of workmanship owing to the unusually high thread count required in the fabric's construction. Generally speaking the lowest count cloth used is 240 threads per square inch, i.e. warp and weft threads combined. The highest thread count is 325 threads per square inch. A wide range of typewriter ribbon fabrics is produced within the 240–325 thread count and, in addition to thread count, the variation involves caliper and weight of yarns.

Pure silk is recommended for applications where clean impressions are necessary as well as long life, e.g. computer output. Nylon fabric is also used to advantage in view of the strength of its fibres which will withstand the heaviest treatment. The impressions are sharp and clean and therefore closely allied to the results obtained from silk.

Ribbons are impregnated with ink of a non drying nature and, therefore, will remain in perfect condition for an indefinite period. All manufacturers use their own formulae for the blending of oils and colours to make the ink for use in their own ribbons and there is no standard ink used throughout the trade.

There has been considerable progress made in developing more specialised dyestuffs for the ribbon trade in the past 20 years and most manufacturers have carried out continual research to improve ink formulae in order to give better impressions, density of colour and also increased life. When assessing the various merits of a ribbon, as much importance should be attached to the quality of ink as to the quality of fabric.

Like most other products, the life of a ribbon depends as much on how it is used as how it was made. Whilst manufacturers maintain a high degree of consistency in the ribbons they make, it is impossible for them to determine exactly the conditions under which each individual ribbon will be used. Therefore a range of fabrics and inking densities is always available to meet individual requirements in respect of operators and machines. The manufacturers are always anxious to give advice on this matter.

Total Release Ribbon

For the preparation of high quality typing for further reproduction other types of ribbon are available. Generally known as coated ribbons, they are in theory total-release, i.e. all, or almost all, of the coating is transferred at a single strike. Base materials used for this class of ribbon are paper or plastics (PVC, polyethylene, mylar, acetate, etc.). Paper ribbons are generally only partial-release, although they can be used once only.

Ribbons for High Quality

The quality of result is directly related to the cost of the ribbon and the kind of material used. Only one-time carbon-coated ribbons (loosely called 'carbon ribbons') give a really crisp, clean impression. There are three main reasons for this: first, they are thinner; second, there is no fabric texture to be reproduced, giving a fuzzy, thickened result; and third, the coating is much drier and consequently the image is less prone to smudging and spreading. One-time ribbons are considerably more expensive than fabric, but are unquestionably far superior in result.

It is very unwise to attempt any economy in ribbons—only the best will give the best results. As an aid to economy in using expensive one-time ribbons, some machines such as the Executive have a proportional ribbon feed with a choice of two feeds: three units for 2- and 3-unit characters, and five units for 4- and 5-unit characters.

Polyethylene is to some extent superseding PVC acetate and mylar as a base. This material, which is imported from the U.S.A., moulds itself around the characters to give a perfect facsimile of the actual type shape. The pigment used is a compound of various oils and waxes with the addition of carbon black. Two ribbons in particular are worth mentioning, IBM 512 and Columbia PF75.

There are different mechanisms for controlling the feed of one-time ribbons and fabric ones, and usually the one-time ribbon attachment is an extra costing several pounds. Machines fitted for one-time ribbons usually have a device to show automatically when the ribbon is nearly used up.

Special-purpose Ribbon

When typing directly on to masters for further reproduction it is essential to use the correct type of ribbon for the reproduction process used. For example when preparing a typed translucent master for subsequent diazo printing a photo-process type fabric ribbon should be used. Although usually black, this type contains some yellow pigment to increase opacity to ultra violet light. To further increase the opacity of image a backing sheet of yellow carbon paper may also be used when typing.

For direct image typing on paper, plastic or metal litho masters, a lithographic ribbon is needed. Dual purpose fabric ribbons are available for use in cases when a machine is required to type a mixture of correspondence and litho masters, but ribbons specially designed to give a sharp, hard-wearing image on a lithographic plate give better results. They are available in fabric and plastic grades, spooled for a wide range of typewriters. Expert advice on the best choice may be sought from the makers of the masters, the machines or the ribbons.

For the typing of hectograph spirit duplicating masters it is often found more economic to use a hectograph typewriter ribbon instead of the usual hectograph carbon backing sheet. This, however, can only be carried out on a machine fitted with a suitable ribbon winding mechanism passing the hectograph ribbon to the rear of the paper master and a normal ribbon at the front.

Sheet Carbons

Carbon paper (a French invention) has been known for nearly a century and a half, but it did not come into full use with the typewriter until the end of the nineteenth century.

As the name implies carbon paper should contain carbon pigment, although today coloured carbon paper is prepared with the aid of various synthetic dyes. However carbon pigment is still most valuable for further document reproduction work. Pseudo-black carbon paper is often dark blue or dark violet and less appropriate for photographic reproduction by an optical system or for contact copying because actinic rays are not sufficiently absorbed by the dyes used.

The pigment is embedded in a fatty substance (e.g. carnauba wax). Carbon paper for copying handwriting usually contains more fatty substance than typewriter carbon paper.

The paper (light carbon paper 10–15 gr. per square metre, heavy paper 16–20 grams or more) should be made of rags and, especially heavy paper, with additional cellulose (25 per cent or more). A good grade of carbon paper should produce at least 12 successive sharp black images on exactly the same spot.

It is obvious that heavy grade carbon paper can give fewer copies at one operation than light, about half the number or less.

The number of carbon-copies to be obtained by ordinary typewriting is normally about five. If very thin copying paper is used and also hard platens perhaps some 10 to 12 copies may be obtained by a good typist on a machine with a sharply cut letter type. With an electrically driven machine the number may go up to 20 copies, but this number is not practical. It is obvious that the thinness of the paper has disadvantages for practical use.

The serious disadvantage of large numbers of carbon copies is the fact that every error has to be erased manually and, as a rule, retyped separately on every carbon.

Carbon copying film sheets are a recent introduction which, although more expensive than conventional paper carbons, are claimed to be economic due to the ease and cleanliness of handling and elimination of waste factor. Caribonum's 'PolyXtra' is available in four varieties, 100 gauge, 50 gauge – for longer life, 50 gauge dense – for blacker copies, and Electric – for use on electric machines.

If carbon copies are to be used for further reproduction purposes they should show an equal blackness of the print. For this purpose the use of carbon-ribbon (paper ribbon) or sets of ribbons may be recommended instead of separate carbon paper sheets to be inserted between the sheets of copying paper.

Apart from the advantage of equality of print, an important labour economy may be obtained by avoiding the hand insertion of layers of carbon paper, which always requires time. Various devices for interposing carbon paper are on the market.

The cost of a carbon copy over the price of the first copy (the "fair" copy) may be estimated to about 1/7 part of the cost of the fair copy. Of course this proportion depends upon wages and material prices and also on the question of whether the typist makes many errors which require extra correction on the carbon copies.

Carbon Paper Alternatives

During the past few years alternative methods to the use of interleaved sheet carbons have been introduced and are now widely used, especially in the field of multiple part stationery systems. The two principle methods are by using carbonised prints or chemical coated papers.

Carbonised prints are simply printed stationery forms with a one-time carbon coating on the back of the form and only on the areas in which information is required to reproduce on the copies. The cost of stationery forms printed in this way is naturally more expensive than normal printed forms but the cost of sheet carbons is eliminated and the saving of labour costs in interleaving helps to offset the additional stationery cost.

Copyfix is a carbon backed paper introduced by Gordon & Gotch Ltd., and it is said to be possible to make 24 copies on this paper using an electric typewriter. There are four different coloured coatings on the backs of five different coloured papers. The copy images are of low contrast, especially when the colour of print is similar to the colour of the paper.

Chemical coated papers were introduced a few years ago by Wiggins Teape under the trade name of NCR (no carbons required) papers. Since then one or two rival products have appeared, including Korofax from Kores Manufacturing Co. Ltd. and Sinecarbon from Gordon & Gotch Ltd. but their introduction is too recent for fair comparative comment to be made here. The following information on the method, therefore, relates only to the Wiggins Teape product.

NCR Papers

NCR paper uses the reaction between two different chemical coatings to produce a copy. The back of the original sheet is coated with one chemical and the top of the second sheet is coated with another chemical. When these two chemicals are brought together they are sensitive to pressure so that anything written or typed on the top sheet is immediately reproduced on the sheet below. This instantaneous reaction is carried right through subsequent sheets of a multi-part set made up on NCR paper.

There are three basic types of N.C.R. paper: the top or original sheet is coated on the back (CB); the middle sheet is coated on both front and back (CFB); and the bottom or last sheet is coated on the front (CF).

In some cases forms on NCR will cost more than the equivalent with one time carbon, but if the application exploits the time-saving qualities of this trouble-free paper, the usual small cost increase is more than offset by increased office efficiency. In this connection it is not always realised that the major cost of business forms occurs when they are being used and handled in an office. The price of the form itself may be as little as 10 per cent of the cost of using it; therefore, any change in the make-up which results in easier and quicker handling—even though it may cost a little more initially—will prove to have been a sound investment.

The cleanliness in handling of coated papers and the smudge proof characteristic of copies in handling is helpful and appreciated by office staff. The chemicals used have been tested and proved to be harmless.

The number of copies obtainable depends on the nature of the form and how it is to be used. For example, handwritten forms on NCR paper should give at least two good copies with pencil and at least three good copies with a ball point pen. With manual typewriter – depending on the typing stroke – you should get at least five good copies. With electric typewriter at least seven good copies. The number of copies indicated above represents a safe starting point for someone who has never used NCR paper before; but, of course, it is known that many people find by experience that they can go well beyond these limits and still get very satisfactory results.

Copies on NCR paper can be erased but not without detection. This is an advantage in certain business forms as it serves as a protection against any alteration of the record. When erasure is necessary, care should be taken not to remove all the coating and the use of a medium rather than a hard eraser is recommended.

The fade resistance of copies on NCR paper is satisfactory for general business documents which may be retained for periods of say four or five years, but it cannot be considered satisfactory for permanent documents required for archival purposes.

The chemical reaction on which NCR paper is based has two distinct phases and two different dyes. The 'blue' dye gives the immediate print and the 'green' dye gives the long term fade resistance. The change-over from 'blue' to 'blue–green' simply means that the long term dyestuff has taken over control. This explains why the shade of the print changes after a time. Contact with water temporarily fades the immediate blue print but after drying, the print returns to its original intensity. Water has no effect on the long term or blue–green print.

The normal precautions taken to protect carbon interleaved forms are usually quite satisfactory for NCR paper. Care should be taken in the shelving of cartons of finished forms to avoid damage to the contents. Under normal storage conditions a shelf life of up to two years is assured.

Generally speaking, NCR paper can be considered for any purpose where more than one copy is required and where the use of this paper offers economic and handling advantages. This covers a wide field from teleprinter rolls to airline tickets, but for most people its advantage lies in more routine application, such as statements, invoices, ledger cards etc.

All types of NCR paper can be printed successfully on offset litho machines and the recent introduction of plain NCR paper in precollated sets now enables any reprographic department with an offset machine to prepare edge gummed sets of forms in two simple operations.

The sheets, as delivered, are collated in reverse order so that they emerge from the litho machine in correct order for padding. This is a simple operation for which no mechanical equipment is necessary. The sets can be hand jogged into a pile, after which a weighted board is placed on top. The adhesive is then brushed on to one edge and left to dry for about ten minutes. Only the coated surfaces adhere to each other and the individual sets can be fanned apart.

CHAPTER VII

OFFICE DUPLICATING

As in other fields of document reproduction, many new discoveries and inventions are rapidly changing the nature of office duplicating. The old order of office duplicating for most requirements up to a few hundred copies, consisted of spirit and stencil duplicating. Offset litho, before the arrival of cheap paper masters, was a printing process reserved for longer runs when higher cost could be set against the need for higher quality. Nowadays offset is in the forefront of duplicating processes, not only in quality but also in versatility and economy.

To use the spirit and stencil processes to duplicate existing documents, it used to be necessary to copy them manually on to an appropriate spirit master or wax stencil. Developments in office copying now enable a duplicating master to be made from practically any kind of original, at only a fraction of the cost of retyping or drawing. The offset litho process has been particularly well served in this respect by the developments in electro photography. The heat transfer process performs a similar service for spirit duplicating and the electronic scanner produces masters for stencil duplicating.

The rapid development of office photocopying processes has also been instrumental in building up a considerable amount of competition to the established duplicating processes. Although office photocopying methods cannot compete economically with duplicating processes when more than half a dozen or so copies are required, they are now widely used for longer runs on the grounds of convenience. Suppliers of office copiers in their sales campaigns have highlighted the fact that present day high wages make manual copying of anything, even by the lower grades of clerical labour, an expensive proposition. Even typewriter carbon copies, beyond the odd one or two, are likely to cost more than photocopies. When copies via a duplicating master for spirit or offset processes are considered, then the savings are even more obvious. How far one can go in ignoring high cost for the sake of convenience is a moot point but there is no doubt that both office copying and duplicating processes aided by photocopy masters will be employed increasingly for ultra short run copying and competition between processes will be keen.

Some of the office photocopying methods have already developed into alternative duplicating processes. Outstanding amongst these are the Adherography process, and the indirect electrostatic process using the sophisticated high speed rotary Xeroduplicator.

The diazo process, although not usually included as an office duplicating process, is also increasing its share of business in this field. Like the spirit and offset processes, it owes some of its increased popularity to the development of office photocopiers which can create translucent masters from most documents enabling multi-copying to be done more cheaply by dyeline in combination with a photocopier than with the photocopier alone. The development of more sophisticated dyeline copiers, easily erased diazo images on translucent material, and cheap litho printed stationery on the new diazo bond papers, have helped the process to attain the recognition it deserves in the field of systems copying.

Still another process taking its place as a duplicating process, particularly in the office systems field, is the 3M Co. Thermofax direct image master and systems copy papers. Both master and copy papers are chemically coated and when contact printed using an infra-red light source copies are produced of similar quality to dye-line. Each master will create a minimum of 25 copies at high speed using the Encore duplicator but copies can be made singly on the standard Thermofax office copier.

From this short review of office duplicating it will be seen that it is no longer easy to draw lines of demarcation between this field of reprography and other forms of document copying. This is particu-larly so when one studies the economics of each process. It then becomes obvious that there is a very close relationship between office photocopying and office duplicating and, in fact, a very considerable area of overlapping occurs at the lower end of the copying scale.

CHAPTER VIII

SPIRIT DUPLICATING

In principle spirit duplicating (or hectography) is a process whereby the text is typed or written with the aid of an alcohol soluble dye-carbon which is transferred to paper in a number of copies. Since the dye is applied only once to the master sheet, this must in one operation receive all the dye necessary for successive copies. It is obvious that this quantity is rather limited.

Whether the copy is typed, written or drawn, the master paper should preferably be a good quality super-calendered grade, reasonably moisture resistant. If the paper is calendered on one side only, it is this side which will receive a laterally reversed image from the dye-carbon sheet as the subject matter is typed or drawn on the opposite side. A variety of colours may be included in the same master by using carbons of different colours. It is not yet possible to produce a black image of any great density.

The main process for obtaining hectograph copies is the spirit (liquid) process. This is more efficient and cleaner than gelatine methods, which it has generally superseded. There are two new methods recently introduced which do not use spirit (referred to later) but they are unlikely to prove generally competitive with the spirit method. Hectography is a somewhat dirty process to operate due to the nature of the dye and any improvement which would eliminate soiling of operators' hands and clothing would probably be welcomed, even at higher cost. The carbon sheet manufacturers have done something to help in this direction by offering carbons with a protective coating over the dye. This assists the person preparing the master but the duplicator operator still has a sensitive master and damp copies to handle carefully if she is to avoid soiling her hands and equipment.

A wide range of spirit duplicating machinery is available using the same basic principle of securing the master, image side out, to a rotating cylinder. Paper is simultaneously fed under a felt pad or a roller system which damps it with spirit, mainly ethyl alcohol. The damp paper is then brought into contact with the master under pressure and this has the effect of transferring a small amount of dye to form the copy image. The sequence may be repeated until all the dye has been removed from the master. Reducing the quantity of solvent on each sheet of paper, or reducing the pressure on the paper as it contacts the master, results in the removal of less dye, giving more copies but with a lighter image. Almost any type and weight of paper can be used provided it does not absorb too much or too little of the solvent.

The number of copies which may be obtained from a master primarily depends on the grade of hectograph carbon used. However, correct operation of the duplicating machine is absolutely essential to obtain the maximum number of copies. A too liberal flow of spirit and incorrect application of the pressure roller may ruin the master before the first dozen copies have been completed.

The length of run under ideal conditions may be up to 300 copies but the spirit process is an economical proposition even though as few as five or six copies are required.

Blue and violet copying inks are most suitable for obtaining a large number of copies. They show two disadvantages; the blue and violet dyes as a rule fade in sunlight; further they do not reproduce well by the usual photographic processes.

When the typing of large numbers of hectograph masters is involved, a considerable saving in cost may be made by using a typewriter fitted with a hectograph carbon roll attachment. This attachment feeds carbon paper from a roll to the back of the master sheet in such a way that the carbon roll is automatically controlled, moving line by line, irrespective of the movement required on the master being prepared. This obviates waste of carbon, particularly on preprinted forms where the typed line spacings may be widely separated. The quantity of carbon paper saved together with the saving of time involved in handling sheet carbons has been found to amount to 70 per cent in certain applications.

Still greater saving in cost can be achieved by using hectograph typewriter ribbons but these can only be used on typewriter machines fitted with a suitable ribbon winding mechanism passing the hectograph ribbon through to the rear of the paper master and a normal ribbon at the front.

If many masters are to be prepared bearing common features, preprinted masters may be obtained by letterpress using hectograph dye inking.

Due to the fact that the number and quality of copies obtainable by this process is so dependent upon the performance of operators, it may be as well to emphasize the following basic principles to be followed.

Preparing the Master

(a) Use good quality one sided Chromo Art faced paper.

(b) Use good quality hectograph carbon of a grade suitable for producing the number of copies required. It is well known that the hectograph process requires much care and cleanliness on the part of the operators due to the copying qualities of the ink. Special care should be taken by operators to keep their hands clean as well as the copies. Hectograph carbons are now available which do tend to minimise this difficulty, but they are rather more expensive than standard carbons grade for grade. Panel coated sheets with an uncoated strip round the edge are cleaner to handle than those entirely coated. Hand creams are available which are formulated specifically to remove carbon soiling.

(c) When correcting an error, the use of a special rubber which absorbs the carbon deposit is a cleaner method than scraping away the error with a razor blade.

(d) The typewriter platen must be in good condition. It is always advisable to use a good quality backing sheet. When using roll carbon attachment, the backing sheet cannot be used but in such cases the standard platen is replaced with a platen made of polythene.

Reproduction

(a) Use the correct grade of spirit for the particular make of carbon used.

(b) Operate the pressure and fluid controls to the minimum which will give sufficient density of image on the copies.

Spirit Masters by Photo-Copy Processes

In recent years the usefulness of office duplicating processes has been extended by the development of methods of making duplicating masters from existing documents.

The first attempts to make hectograph spirit masters from existing originals were via the ferro gelatine or TTS process. The process was too messy to become a commercial proposition but the arrival of

Xerography led to another possible answer in the form of a spirit master created from an electrostatic image. This image is transferred from a selenium plate to a dye carbon sheet on a Xerox 1385 Processor (see page 121). The image is vapour fused in a Flo-set unit in contact with a sheet of master material under a pressure roller, the image becoming fused to both carbon dye and master paper. Separation of carbon sheet and master leaves a good deposit of dye on the master sheet giving quite lengthy duplicating runs. Although the process is effective, the cost of equipment needed and the time required makes it uneconomic nowadays.

The first economically successful method of facsimile spirit master making came as an additional facility offered by the infra-red document copying process. As with all heat transfer machines, the original must have a metallic or carbon content and it is not possible, therefore, to make masters from originals prepared with coloured inks. The carbon used is heat-sensitive. It is placed with the master on top of the original and passed through the copier. The metallic or carbon content of the image on the original absorbs the heat more readily than the background, causing the hectograph carbon to melt in the image area and adhere to the master paper. Only purple carbon on a very flimsy tissue with no metal content is successful. Black spirit carbon does not work successfully because heat is generated over the whole surface giving a black background to the master.

Spirit masters prepared in this way still lack the sharpness of image required to produce really good quality hectograph copies, but legible copies from reasonable originals can be expected, especially when they have been prepared with a hard pencil, say 3H or 4H grade. Heat process carbons on a nylon base, although expensive compared with paper base, do give clearer, sharper copies.

The carbon master sets supplied for this process are of a flimsy nature and the finished masters are difficult to manage without creasing on some duplicators. An alternative method, if the original is typed on tracing paper, is to feed it through the copier with a sheet of transfer carbon as a backing sheet – carbon side to the back of the original. This puts a layer of dye on the back of the original and it can itself then be used as the duplicating master. The process can be repeated with the same original for further runs if required.

The introduction of heat process spirit masters offers a very satisfactory way of getting around the unpopularity with clerks and typists of spirit duplicating. A document can be prepared on a clean sheet of paper and the dye put on afterwards quite cheaply.

Diffusion Transfer Method

Another new method of preparing hectograph masters is by the diffusion transfer process. In the Agfa version, the original is exposed with a sheet of hectograph negative paper and this is developed in contact with a sheet of special positive paper. After separation the positive is ready to put on the duplicator. The Gevaert process is more lengthy and expensive. It involves processing the negative in a special developer and then squeezing it against a sheet of normal master paper. After separation, only a short interval is needed before using the master on a duplicator. The use of a special thermo-statically controlled processing unit is recommended and the master costs about 2s. 0d. so it is unlikely to compete with the simpler Agfa method in which the master costs 25 per cent less.

Dry Hectography

There are two spiritless versions of the hectograph process but owing to their limitations neither are likely to compete seriously with the spirit version. The Azograph process by A. B. Dick uses three components of a diazo dye which are colourless until coupling takes place in the machine. In the wax image of the master, a non-soluble colour is incorporated to make it visible and the copy colour is royal blue. The process is only satisfactory for about 30 copies.

In the Drimatic process by Ellams, the master is treated with an antistatic compound and a dry solvent is incorporated in the copy paper. Copy production is similar to spirit duplicating but the copies are clean to handle as they leave the machine. The material to be duplicated is typed, written or drawn on a master set devised to avoid any contact between the operator's hands and the carbon sheet. Each master will provide from 100 to 150 copies. The duplicator is available in hand feed and auto feed versions at £30 and £50 respectively. A variable pressure control is provided to assist in image control when longer runs are required.

Spirit Duplicating Machines

The wide range of spirit duplicating machines available may be broadly classified into three main groups.

1. Hand operated portable machines.
2. Electrically operated machines.
3. Electrically operated systems or line selecting machines.

(Top left) Ormig D 460 MTA

Two independent auto feeds. Takes brief or 2 fscp. Copy counter. Loads ½ ream. Var. registration. Clamping for masks & additional masters.

(Top right) Fordigraph 603

Hand feed, copy return model. Foot pedal control. Re-set copy-counter. Var. registration. Auto fluid control.

(Middle) Banda 900

Ream feed. High speed master change. Auto cut-off & copy counter. Auto feed. Dial pressure and fluid.

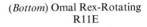

(Bottom) Omal Rex-Rotating R11E

All feeds automatic including master load/reject. Secondary feed for accurate register. Single sheet feed facility.

SOME ELECTRICALLY OPERATED SPIRIT DUPLICATORS

(*Top*) The Anson Ormig
Selectronic 11

Random Line Selecting Machine.
Offers a wide combination of pre-set
programmes or random selection.

(*Middle*) The Anson Ormig D.2300
and D.3600 Series Syste n Machines
have dual clamps for masters and
variable masters, operated by single
control.

(*Bottom*) Banda Selectomatic AP

Auto Programmed Line Select with
extensive push button features. 32
lines selection. Front] delivery copies
max. size 17″ × 13½″. Auto feed
optional.

SOME ELECTRIC LINE SELECTION AUTOMATIC SYSTEMS
DUPLICATORS

Within the hand operated and electrically operated groups, some machines are offered in two alternative forms, hand feed or automatic feed. In the systems group there is a very wide range of models providing varying degrees of automation by line selection and simultaneous use of more than one master. Some of these machines are equipped with electronic control panels enabling a random selection of lines on the master to be printed in sequence, or a series of lines to be automatically printed in sequential progression. At least one is equipped with a photo electric scanner activated by marks made on the master using up to five channels in addition to preset machine programmes.

The following examples of spirit duplicating machines were not selected because they have particular advantages over those of other manufacturers but simply because they are within the groups mentioned.

SOME HAND-OPERATED SPIRIT DUPLICATING MACHINES

Model & Supplier	Features
Banda 15 Block & Anderson Ltd.	Roller damping; automatic paper feed; easy adjustment.
Ormig D.17 Geo. Anson & Co. Ltd.	4-position pressure control; automatic paper feed; auto fluid control. D.16 hand feed version.
Consul Automatic Office Mechanisation Ltd.	Auto fluid pump from sealed container; metal moistening roller; auto paper feed; variable registration. Consul Standard hand feed version.
Hector Automatic Ellams Duplicator Co. Ltd.	Pad to roller damping; variable pressure; automatic paper feed. Hector hand feed version.
Piccolo Skycopy	Inexpensive portable; pad damping.
Rex-Rotary R11H Office Machinery Ltd.	Auto feed or single sheet; secondary precision feed. Suitable for simple systems work.
Ambassador Office Mechanisation Ltd.	Auto fluid; all major controls in single unit; counter; auto feed; closing machine disengages rollers. Electric model available.

CHAPTER IX

STENCIL DUPLICATING

The use of stencils enables copies to be made in quantities of less than 100 to a few thousands. The master stencil can be prepared by any skilled typist on any ordinary typewriter. The printing machine does not require a skilled operator.

The stencil process is designed for office reproduction of medium size editions and moderate use, so that for quantities of 100 to 1000 copies this process may be considered as being reasonably cheap where the number of pages to be copied each year does not justify the purchase of offset equipment. For small editions hectograph and other processes may be preferable. For large quantities or, where better quality of reproduction is required, other processes of reproduction should be used.

Two disadvantages of the stencil process are that it is generally necessary to use a thick semi absorbent paper and that a certain amount of ink is wasted owing to the amount unused on the finished stencil.

The first stencil was invented in 1881. It was a sheet of thin waxed paper which could be written on with a steel stylus, the wax being removed along the line of writing. A sheet of absorbent tissue was laid over the stencil and together they were stretched in a wooden frame. A sheet of paper was placed underneath, an inked roller passed over it and a copy obtained. Its advantage over the hectograph process was that a much larger number of prints could be obtained from the one writing.

By 1888 a stencil suitable for use on a typewriter was produced. The coating was still wax which caused considerable inconvenience due to the type becoming rapidly choked with wax. To minimise this trouble an additional sheet of thin tissue was interposed between the type and the stencil.

This produced blurred impressions and other methods were tried such as painting the stencil with developing fluid and even filing down the type characters to reduce their sharpness. However, it was not until around 1920 that any reliable stencil was produced. It was known as the "indestructible" stencil but even this product did not get off to an easy start due to the fact that it had to be wetted before cutting. Typists did not take kindly to this procedure and the "dry indestructible" stencil soon followed and came to stay. Some wax stencils are still employed, principally on the score of cheapness, but the bulk of stencils now used are made of mulberry or manila fibres coated with cellulose derivatives.

During the lengthy period of development of the stencil, the duplicator itself continued to improve. The stretching frame became the hinged flat bed, sometimes still seen today, and by the turn of the century the first of the rotary duplicators appeared. Many types of rotary stencil duplicators are now available, both hand operated and electrically driven. The hand operated machine may have a theoretical production capacity of 75 copies per minute whilst electrically driven machines may theoretically produce up to 7500 copies per hour. However, it should be borne in mind that other factors such as the changing or replacing of stencils influence the practical production rates. A simple rule for calculating the number of copies which may be achieved per hour whilst making a series of short runs is to multiply the number of copies per run by 10. Thus with a series of stencils of which 35 copies of each are required, the production rate would be approximately 350 per hour. The figures may be increased very considerably for electrically operated machines.

The flat bed, apart from the stamp type used for addressing, is of very limited use. Its only advantage is a facility for very accurate registration and it may be used with success for multi-coloured copies (e.g. maps) in small numbers.

In the rotary machine, the master stencil is fastened to an inked drum, the image facing inwards. On the older machines the need for frequent inking up of the ink pad restricted their operational output but nowadays the ink is usually contained in the cylinder and soaks through perforations into an ink distributing pad on the outside of the drum. Devices are incorporated for increasing ink flow through parts of the stencil needing it. Another system of inking uses a series of rollers to carry ink on to a silk belt passing around two cylinders, the stencil being carried on the outside of the belt. In this system an ink paste is used which gives a sharper image than the liquid ink used on single cylinder machines.

There have been many developments in the design of stencil duplicators to improve speed and accuracy, but the overriding considera-

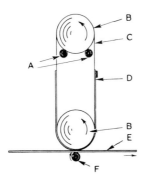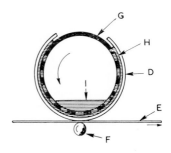

ROTARY DUPLICATORS

The two cylinder model (*left*) uses ink paste on a moving belt as opposed
to the liquid ink reservoir of the single cylinder machine (*right*).

A. Ink distributing rollers. B. Solid cylinder. C. Silk carrier for stencil.
D. Stencil. E. Copy paper. F. Pressure roller. G. Hollow perforated
cylinder. H. Absorbent ink distributing pad. I. Ink.

tion is always simplicity of operation so that a reasonable standard of
work can be obtained by an operator with a minimum of training.
The machine must always be ready for immediate use, require a
minimum of cleaning down after use and little or no maintenance. It
is in this field that the stencil duplicator has an advantage over offset
litho.

In all rotary machines, paper is fed through the machine with each
rotation and is pressed against the stencil by a pressure roller,
squeezing ink through the open image areas of the stencil. The paper
must be absorbent to minimise offsetting of the image from one sheet
to another in the receiving tray. Esparto paper is normally used and
this is more expensive than many of the papers used in other forms of
duplicating. Papers which are not so absorbent can also be used if
interleaved with an absorbent paper as copies are made, or if sprayed
with a drying powder. Modern duplicators are capable of copying on
to a reasonably wide range of papers from lightweight to card.
Coloured inks can be used and multicoloured copies prepared if
spare master cylinders are available for changing master stencils, and
some trouble is taken to achieve registration, always a difficult
matter on friction feed machines.

The cost of stencil duplicating is higher than in spirit duplicating
and the latter is a more versatile process. However, the stencil process provides more permanent copies of better quality and in longer

runs. Compared with offset duplicating, the stencil process has two advantages, the capital cost is lower and the duplicator can be used by any girl in the office. This must be set against the higher copy cost of stencil duplicating compared with those from an offset duplicator.

Duplicating Inks

A primary consideration in formulating duplicator inks is that they should be non-drying on the machine itself, so that however long a machine stands without use, the ink will remain in a workable condition in drums, inking cloths, distributing rollers, etc. In other processes for printing on paper, a variety of physical and chemical means can be used to achieve drying of the ink in contact with the paper. These include

1. Absorption of liquid constituents of the ink by the paper.
2. Evaporation of liquid constituents of the ink.
3. Air oxidation resulting in hardening of the ink.
4. "Setting" of the ink by absorption of moisture from the paper.

DRYING METHODS OF VARIOUS INKS

Printing Process	Absorption	Evaporation	Air oxidation	Moisture setting
Letterpress printing	√		√	
"Moisture set" letterpress inks	√			√
Offset litho	√		√	
Rotogravure printing	√	√		
Newsprint inks	√			
Stencil duplicating inks	√			

Duplicating inks dry only by absorption into the paper. Any other of the mechanisms listed would eventually result in drying out on the machine itself.

By comparison with other printing processes, stencil duplicating deposits a relatively thick layer of ink on the paper and rapid absorption of this by the paper is needed to avoid smudging or offset onto the back of the following copy. The absorbency of ordinary printing papers, banks and bonds is not high enough for this purpose and papers specially manufactured for duplicating should be used wherever possible. When the liquid medium of the ink is absorbed it penetrates through the thickness of the paper and to some extent spreads sideways from the outline of the printed character. By using an uncoloured liquid medium for the ink and a solid pigment colour, this "strike through" and spreading is not normally visible and the duplicated character remains sharp on drying.

Duplicating Ink

Solid pigment colour

←— Duplicator Paper —→

Liquid Ink medium
(invisible)

INK DRYING

When first deposited on the paper, the liquid ink rests on the surface. The oil medium is then rapidly absorbed, leaving the solid pigment on the paper.

The liquid ink medium of a duplicator ink is usually a non-volatile oil. The lower the viscosity of the oil, the more rapid the drying. Low viscosity oils do not, however, produce inks with good printing properties and the medium used in present day quick drying duplicating inks is usually an emulsion of water in oil. The emulsion breaks down in contact with the paper and allows rapid penetration of the constituents into the paper.

The consistency of inks for a single cylinder duplicator differ from that required for a two cylinder machine, the former being referred to as a liquid ink and the latter "paste" ink. Although paste inks give a somewhat sharper impression it has not so far been possible to formulate these to penetrate into the paper and dry as rapidly as liquid inks. Speed of drying is one of the main advantages claimed for the single cylinder machine. Another is economy in ink consumption.

The consistency of liquid inks must be very carefully standardised in manufacture to maintain the correct rate of flow from the inside of the cylinder through the distributing cloth and the perforations in the stencil. The consistency is somewhat sensitive to temperature variations which can lead to ink starvation in cold climates or excessive inking in hot climates and for this reason manufacturers provide a range of inks to cover normal working temperatures in different parts of the world.

Black is by far the most important "colour" for duplicating inks and carbon black is the pigment in general use which gives the copies a very high degree of permanence. They are resistant to light fading and erasures by chemical treatment. Other colours are, however, becoming increasingly popular and manufacturers supply a full range. Organic pigment dyestuffs are used for these and they are selected for brightness of shade, stability and freedom from tendency to bleed in the medium which would result in a coloured halo round the copy.

Automatic Inking Mechanisms

In two cylinder machines the "paste" ink is fed onto the outside of one or other of the cylinders and distributed in an even film over the surface both by the carrier silk and one or more distributing rollers running in contact with the cylinder. Under pressure from the pressure roller the ink is forced through the carrier silk and stencil on to the copy paper and on these machines the automatic inking device must supply to the cylinder a precise amount of ink according to the number and size of the perforations in the stencil.

The ink is forced from the container via a tube perforated at intervals on to the cylinder either by a suction pump (Gestetner 360) or pressure on a piston in the container itself (Rex D.270). A calibrated adjustment is provided to vary the amount of ink delivered according to the requirements of the stencil and some judgement on the part of the operator is necessary to obtain the correct setting for this. The ink demand may vary considerably across the stencil and a

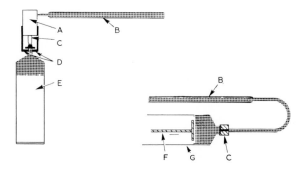

AUTOMATIC INKING SYSTEMS
The Gestetner method (*left*) uses a suction pump to force ink from the container.
The Rex D270 (*right*) uses a pressure-operated piston in the container.
A. Pump. B. Distribution tube. C. Air tight seal. D. Supports for tube.
E. Lead tube containing ink. F. Piston. G. Ink container.

90

selection switch is provided so that the ink supply to sections of the cylinder can be cut off as required.

The principle of inking is quite different in a single cylinder machine. The liquid ink is contained inside the cylinder and passes through perforations into the ink distributing cloth which is made from a comparatively thick absorbent material. When the cloth is compressed by the pressure roller, ink is forced out and passes through the perforations in the stencil and any surplus in the neighbourhood of uncut areas of the stencil is returned through the cylinder perforations to the inside of the cylinder.

This return of ink automatically compensates for any varying demand of the stencil and no adjustment to the ink supply is needed, whether a single word is cut on the stencil or it is typed over the whole working area. The rate of flow of ink through the distributing cloth and the density of copy can vary according to the amount of ink inside the cylinder and this variation is avoided in the Ellams copy controlled inking CCI system by retaining the bulk of the ink in a reservoir inside the cylinder and supplying this as a constant thin layer on the inside wall of the cylinder when rotated. When the machine is at rest there is no surplus ink to seep through the perforations of the cylinder and flood the machine. The system also provides a means for supplying additional ink to the cloth where exceptional demands are made by very heavily cut stencils.

Stencils and their Preparation

A stencil set consists of three parts, the headpiece, the stencil itself and the backing sheet. The headpiece is the attachment which anchors the stencil to the duplicator. It is perforated with holes or slots which fit an arrangement of pegs on the duplicator of which each make has its own particular pattern. Stencils for use on flat bed duplicators have no headpiece.

The stencil usually consists of a thin tough, fibrous paper base, which is impregnated with the supplier's own formula of "melt". The backing sheet is of stout paper attached to the headpiece. It serves as a backing sheet whilst the stencil is being typed and is used to receive the first rough impression from the duplicator. It is detached by tearing along a perforated line before the run of copies commences.

A few sheets of carbon paper are usually included with the stencils and one of these coated side upwards, is interleaved between stencil and backing sheet for the typing operation. The carbon has several functions, first to make the typing easier to read and check, and

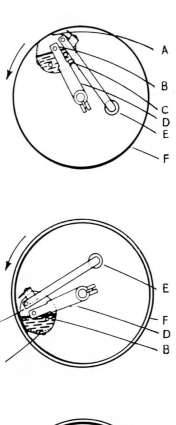

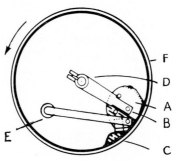

ELLAMS CCI INKING SYSTEM

Top: Inker off, machine at rest. *Middle:* Inker on, normal operating position.
Bottom: Inker on, booster position for very heavily cut stencils.

A. Ink trough. B. Trough pivot. C. Ink. D. Trough support. E. Counter-
balance weight. F. Perforated cylinder.

92

secondly to check the chopping out of enclosed characters which can occur if the type face is too sharp or the typist's touch too heavy. One carbon will serve its purpose for a number of stencils.

A thin transparent Cellophane sheet or ribbon placed in front of the stencil, is sometimes used to avoid cutting out enclosed characters. It has the added advantage of keeping the type face clean. Most stencils are printed with frame lines and register scales to assist the typist in correctly positioning her work in relation to the paper size used for the copies. Instructions to the typist on this point could well be included in the standards suggested in Chapter I.

The cutting of a good stencil requires experience on the part of the typist and an adequately serviced typewriter. Clean clear type is extremely important. Typebar machines are more suitable than those employing type elements or shuttles. Electrically operated typebar machines are particularly suitable due to the even pressure and facility for adjustment which they provide. Broad type faces should be avoided and any type with closer spacing than 12 to the inch should be treated with respect if a stencil full of blind o's is to be avoided. The type styles known as "gothics" require a much lighter touch than the "romans" on account of their simplified outlines and absence of serifs. The hardness of the platen also has a bearing on the pressure of stroke needed. A hard platen requires a lighter touch than a medium platen. Other things being equal, the typestroke should be slightly heavier for stencils than for normal ribbon typing on paper. Another requirement which tests the skill of the typist when using non-electric machines is the need to vary the stroke according to the character. A heavier stroke is needed for characters such as the M, H, W and all fractions, than for o, c, e, i and punctuations.

A high typing speed should not be attempted when preparing stencils, simply because accuracy and quality are more important when perhaps 500 or more copies are to be made from the one typing. Fortunately, corrections at the typing stage can be made fairly easily by painting out the error with a blocking fluid and retyping over it. The correcting fluid should not be used over a wide area as it contracts in drying and puckers the stencil. An alternative method for major corrections is to cut out the area of error, retype on the bottom edge of a new stencil and cut this out slightly larger than the area of error, match it in the required position and secure with a touch of correcting fluid around the edges. This operation requires a razor blade and a steady hand. It is recommended only as a last resort to retyping a whole stencil, as the effort may still be wasted by a mishap when the graft is stressed on the duplicator.

It is often necessary to write or draw on a stencil, if only to produce a passable specimen of a signature. For this purpose tools are available in the form of wheel pens and steel styli. When using them a hardish backing sheet is required such as a sheet of plastic. With the right texture of backing sheet it is even possible to draw lines, of limited length, with a ball point pen but a wheel pen is less restrictive for this purpose. Using a steel stylus for signatures requires a little practice which should not be gained in signing completely typed stencils!

When regular use is made of the same format, e.g. stationery forms and financial returns, pre-cut stencils bearing the common information and rulings, can be ordered from the stencil supplier. These stencils are prepared by impressing with printers type but they are economical only when supplied in quantity for a particular printed style.

There are some special varieties of stencil, available for applications not catered for in the standard range. One of these is a specially sensitive type for use on noiseless typewriters, which do not cut ordinary stencils well owing to their weak striking action. These stencils require handling with care, and do not give such a long run of copies.

For handwriting a special double coated stencil is available. The first coating is white and a face coating is in a strongly contrasting colour so that when they are cut with styli and ruling pens, the image becomes easily visible as work progresses. There are also tracing stencils which have a degree of translucency for copying originals placed beneath them.

Diapositive stencils provide a convenient method of preparing metal plates for offset litho machines. They are coated with a composition containing pigments which are opaque to ultra-violet light. This coating can be cut in a typewriter and the cut stencil used in place of the usual film negative in printing down the offset plate.

A most important development in the field of stencil duplicating has been the invention of the electronic stencil cutter. For this, another new kind of stencil was required containing electrically conductive pigments, usually a form of carbon black. There is no fall out of letters because cutting consists of a series of minute perforations, well separated, but the stencils are somewhat fragile and should be handled carefully.

Electronic Stencil Cutter

Until the introduction of the electronic stencil cutter, stencil duplication was limited virtually to that which could be cut on a stencil either by typewriting or drawing with a stylus. Admittedly the stencil made by photographic means made a brief appearance a few years ago but did not achieve any widespread popularity.

With the electronic stencil cutter it is possible to produce a stencil from almost any form of document and even photographs. Further, it is possible to duplicate in more than one colour by separating the colours on the original and making separate stencils for each colour on the electronic scanner. A modern duplicator providing fairly accurate registration is necessary, of course, for running the copies.

The electronic stencil cutter consists of a rotating cylinder on which the original to be copied and a specially coated stencil are positioned side-by-side. As this rotates the original is scanned by a photo-electric cell synchronised with a spark gap scanning the stencil. When the photo-electric cell senses a dark area, a series of pin-point holes is burned in the stencil thus forming the same pattern as the original.

Definition is controlled by altering the pitch of scanning; typescript or print can be satisfactorily copied at around 125 lines per inch whereas a more complex original may require 250 lines per inch and a photograph perhaps 500 to 750 lines to the inch. A screened photograph makes a more satisfactory subject than a continuous tone one. The lower the pitch, the faster the stencil will be cut. Using the highest pitch the process may take 15 to 20 minutes to complete a $10'' \times 8''$ picture but at the lowest pitch only about 5 to 10 minutes. The machine needs no attention once the cycle has been started and, therefore, chargeable labour cost is small. The operator can be performing other duties meanwhile, and be informed of completion of the stencil by an alarm bell.

The first electronic stencil cutters to be introduced have all been designed with variable pitch control but, more recently, cutters with fixed pitch and simplified controls have been developed to exploit more widely the new potential of cheap stencil duplicating facilitated by this new invention.

Examples of the variable pitch machines are the Gestetner 455, Omal Electrorex and the Roneotronic. The fixed pitch machines are the Gestetner ES.390 and the Ellams Vellafax 220.

The ES.390 has a simple three press button system, On–Start–Stop. It has a scan pitch of 200 lines per inch but at a fast cutting speed of 52 seconds per inch, enabling an average subject of 7 inches width to be cut in 6 minutes. As previously mentioned, quality of copy is directly related to scanning pitch and, therefore, fixed pitch cutters have their limitations in image definition and are only intended to offer a compromise in acceptable quality of copy and fast rate of stencil production.

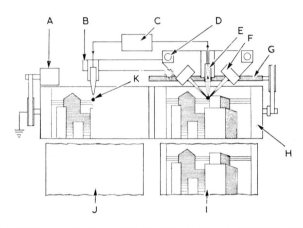

SCHEMATIC DIAGRAM OF GESTETNER ES.390 STENCIL CUTTER

A. Drum motor. B. Scanning carriage. C. Amplifier. D. Exciter lamp. E. Electronic eye. F. Lens. G. Lead screw. H. Copy and stencil drum. I. Original to be copied. J. Stencil.

The Vellafax 220 machine has a scanning pitch of 254 lines per inch and a cutting speed of 75 seconds per inch. It is equipped with power control, background control and output control knobs, all of which must be set to a reading on a meter before cutting starts. This arrangement enables different types of stencil, plastic or fibre, to be used and also enables a balance of quality to be achieved from a wide variety of originals.

Stencil Duplicating Machines

The stencil duplicating process is not adaptable to complex office systems work and there are no machines built specifically for this purpose as is the case with spirit duplicators. Stencil duplicating machines fall naturally into two general categories, single cylinder

(*Top*) Vellafax Model 220

Maximum copy area 13¼ in. × 10 in.
Fixed scanning pitch 254 lines,
per inch.

(*Middle*) Roneotronic

Maximum copy area 13 in. × 8 in.
Scanning control 200 to 500 lines
per inch.

(*Bottom*) Omal 354 Stencil Cutter

Maximum copy area 13¼ in. × 8½ in.
Scanning variable between 100 and
1000 lines per inch. Will also make
a litho plate.

ELECTRONIC STENCIL CUTTERS

(*Top*) Gestetner 455

Maximum copy area 14 in. × 8½ in. Three scanning speeds.—200/400/600 giving cutting speeds of 45, 90 or 130 secs. per inch.

(*Middle*) Omal RR 2000 Stencil Cutter

Fixed scanning pitch 200 lines per inch.

(*Bottom*) Omal RR 2200 Stencil Cutter

Maximum copy area 8½ in. × 12½ in. Variable scanning 125 to 750 lines per inch. Switch control to make negative stencil.

ELECTRONIC STENCIL CUTTERS

and two cylinder, each including both hand operated and powered models. Some powered machines may also be hand operated.

The Gestetner range of two cylinder machines is an integrated series ranging from de luxe electric models to the basic hand-operated version, but all with the essential mechanisms identical throughout.

There are many practical advantages in this scheme such as inter-changeability of parts and simplification of maintenance service. The Model 300 is a basic foolscap hand-operated machine, the 310 a single-speed, electrically-operated version, and the 320 a low-cost, two-speed machine. The 360 is a powered version with infinitely variable speed up to 150 copies per minute and many other refinements, whilst the 330 is its hand-operated version. The Model 366 incorporates all the features of the 360 but is equipped additionally with a secondary feed between the primary feed and the pressure roller to give extreme accuracy of registration. The Model 466 is a restyled version of the 366. It incorporates several major improvements including automatic ink feed and paper feed.

The range extends to double-foolscap models and in this field Gestetner also offer a machine called the Newsprinter, specially

GESTETNER MODEL 366

A fscp. two cylinder electric machine. Variable speed to 150 cpm. Interleaver drive and precision secondary feed.

99

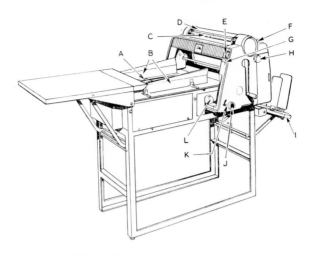

THE GESTETNER NEWSPRINTER

A large two cylinder machine with a max. print area of $16\frac{3}{4}'' \times 11''$
A. Feeder bar. B. Conveyor side guides. C. Ink screen heading. D. Ink
screen. E. Print height adjuster. F. Inking lever. G. Feed lever. H. Ink
selector. I. Collecting tray. J. Speed control knob. K. Switch lever.
L. Timing gear knob.

designed to allow stop press items to be overprinted locally on
newspapers.

The Omal Rex-Rotary range is also of two cylinder design.

The principal features of the Ellams single cylinder machine are the
copy controlled inking system described earlier in this chapter, and
the continuous stream-feeding of paper which allows reloading without interruption. Various thicknesses and sizes of paper, and even
thin card can be fed without stopping the machine. An anti-set-off
spray attachment is available.

The wide range of Roneo machines all exploit the rapid colour
change facility of single cylinder machines. Many automatic features
are included to eliminate much of the need for operator skill and
attention. The Model 865 illustrated on p. 101 fully complies with
the safety regulations contained in the Offices, Shops and Railway
Premises Act 1963, and BSI Specification 3861.

(*Top left*) Omal Rex Rotary D490

Two cyl. var. speed to 100 cpm. Auto inking. Secondary precision reed. Optional autocollator/interleaver. Pre-set counter.

(*Top right*) Ellams Speed-Rite

Single cyl. CCI inking. Pre-set counter. Auto feed paper 3″ × 3″ to 9″ × 14″ Variable speed control. Quick colour change facility.

(*Middle*) Roneo 865

Single cyl. var. speed 40–160 cpm. Single lever control. Auto or hand feed. Power or hand operated. Pre-set counter plus totalisator. Delivery tray jogger. 25 second colour change.

(*Bottom*) Roneo 795

Single cyl. var. speed 40–100 cpm of brief size. Fully automatic or hand operated. Takes two fscp stencils side by side or one fscp only. 25 second colour change.

SOME ELECTRICALLY OPERATED STENCIL
DUPLICATORS

CHAPTER X

OFFSET LITHO DUPLICATING

Lithography is one of the major printing processes and one of the oldest. It falls within the category of flat printing processes as opposed to letterpress which uses raised type, and gravure using an etched or sunken image.

With letterpress, or relief printing, the raised parts of the type surface are coated with printer's ink, which is then transferred to paper, whereas in gravure, or deep printing, the whole plate is inked, wiped clean, and the ink remaining in the etched or sunken portions is transferred to paper under pressure. With the flat printing process, however, as the name suggests, there are no differences of depth, the inked image being created on the actual surface of the printing plate.

How Litho Works

The principle of lithography is the creation of a moisture repellent image on a moisture retaining surface. Since water and grease will not mix, the image attracts the greasy printing ink applied to it by inking rollers, but water applied and retained in other areas repels the ink, thus allowing a copy to be made when paper is brought into contact with the image. In earlier years lithography involved the use of a porous stone bed which was able to retain sufficient moisture to repel the ink in the unwanted areas. Later this was replaced by a zinc plate treated in the same manner. There are now several variations of the lithographic process and this earlier form is now correctly described as flat bed direct lithography.

The direct method of lithography has one disadvantage in that it requires the image on the printing plate to be in reverse. An American printer noticed that after his direct litho machine had been running idle with no paper passing through, the first sheet of paper of the subsequent run picked up an image on its reverse side from the pressure roller. He observed that this image, although in reverse appeared better than those obtained from the zinc bed. This marked the beginning of offset lithography, which has since become the most popular process in this class of printing. With modern offset machines the image is transferred from the plate to a rubberised fabric surface on a cylinder, and thence to the paper.

Direct lithography has not become a popular office process despite the advantages which can be claimed for this method. These are the simplicity of construction and rapid machine preparation made possible by eliminating the offset blanket and cylinder. The need to make a reverse-reading master image has been catered

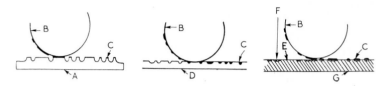

TRADITIONAL PRINTING METHODS

Letterpress (*left*) prints from a relief image, gravure (*centre*) from a recessed image and litho (*right*) from a flat image.
A. Block. B. Paper. C. Ink. D. Gravure plate. E. Moisture. F. Grease image. G. Litho stone.

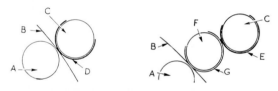

ROTARY LITHO METHODS

Lithography can use a direct method (*left*) with reversed image on the printing plate or an indirect, offset method (*right*).
A. Impression cylinder. B. Paper. C. Plate cylinder. D. Litho plate. E. Offset litho plate. F. Blanket cylinder. G. Rubber blanket.

for by using a thin metal plate with a sheet of greased carbon placed behind it so that the action of the typewriter key deposits a greasy image on the back of the plate. This method of master making resembles that used in the spirit duplicating process. The plate is attached to the machine with the reverse image facing outwards. When it is inked and paper passed over it, copies are produced in either short runs or long runs up to 20,000 or so copies. Photographically prepared plates from film negatives can be used to produce up to 50,000 copies of good quality.

The advantages of offset printing, compared with the use of a direct impression, are two fold. Improved quality of the impressions and protection of the printing plate, which never comes into contact with the paper at all. The technique of offset printing, which goes back less than 50 years, has developed very rapidly and already acquired a pre-eminent position in office duplicating, as well as for colour work in graphic art.

Offset Methods

About 25 years ago it was decided to adopt the offset technique for small duplicating machines now indispensible in office work. Originally, metallized sheets were typewritten with a special ribbon and then used in the offset machine. The good results obtained soon encouraged the adoption of photographic transfers for the printing sheets; as a result these offset machines, originally designed as duplicators, were found to have many new applications.

The printing plate is not subjected to any appreciable stresses in the modern offset duplicating machine, so it can be made of any lightweight material provided the surface is, or can be made, moisture-retaining whilst the base is sufficiently non-absorbent to retain its strength and form. Papers, plastics and plasticised papers are now all used in addition to aluminium and zinc alloys.

Paper masters are cheap and available in various grades, the cheaper grades being suitable for office systems work, giving up to a hundred copies whilst the superior grades will provide some thousands of copies. Paper masters are usually discarded after running although they can be stored for limited re-use if necessary. In such cases it is advisable to reinforce the gripping edge as they are inclined to break away at this point under repeated wetting.

Properly imaged metal plates produce tens of thousands of copies and can be stored for repeated use.

There is a very wide range of offset litho duplicators and presses and the functions they carry out overlap very considerably. This often confuses the potential user to the extent of installing a machine which he considers will serve a dual purpose, only to find that it is too costly in labour for his primary application and inadequate to fill the needs of his secondary application.

Office Offset Machines

Within the field of what is generally accepted as being small or office offset litho machines, there are three main groupings.

1. General purpose office machines.

These are the least expensive machines costing between £400

and £600 and they fill a need for short run duplicating in an office systems application where 150 to 200 masters a day are produced. Alternatively this machine will print long runs of stationery forms or circulars, even in multicolour if sufficient white space is left between the colours for small inaccuracies not to be revealed.

2. Systems offset duplicators.

These are the more expensive office machines designed for automatic or semi-automatic operation and costing around £1300 to £3000. They are usually manufacturers' standard models with many accessories and automatic control features added. Masters can be changed in about 10 seconds as against a minute or so on standard machines. Inking up, blanket cleaning and number of copies run from each master are automatically controlled and consequently very little skill is needed in the operator. However, the machines are fairly complex and there should be a skilled person available somewhere in the background to act as a trouble-shooter if breakdown time is to be kept to a minimum. If a machine of this type, handling up to 500 systems masters a day, is out of action for even a few hours, the hold-up is likely to have serious repercussions somewhere.

3. Offset printing machines.

The main differences in these machines from those in Group 1 are their heavier inking capability, hairline registration and greater versatility in image control generally. Many of these machines are used in internal print departments both for long run printing and high grade short run duplicating from direct image and photo masters. The price range extends from the upper limit of Group 1 and overlaps that of Group 2 according to mechanical features and print size catered for.

Offset Mechanical Systems

In all offset litho machines there are four mechanical systems. They are found in their simplest practical form in the cheaper machines and in more elaborate forms in the more expensive models. These four systems are the water or dampening system, the inking system, the print cylinders and the paper feeding mechanism.

Each system has its own operating and adjustment controls.

Before considering the functions of each system let us consider the sequence in which they operate to produce a copy after the master has been mounted on the plate cylinder.

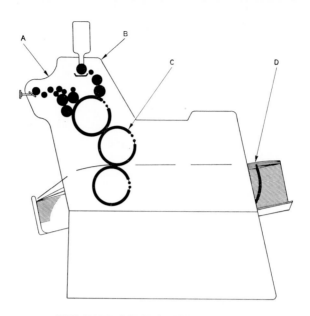

THE FOUR MECHANICAL SYSTEMS
A. Inking. B. Dampening. C. Printing cylinders. D. Paper feeding.

First, a thin film of water or dilute chemical fountain solution is applied all over the surface of the plate. It is held by the non-image areas but repelled by the greasy image area. Following this, the inking roller is brought into contact with the plate. The ink is held by the image area but is repelled by the dampened non-image area. This ink is then passed by contact, forming a reverse image upon the rubber blanket on the blanket cylinder. Meanwhile a sheet of paper is delivered by the paper feed mechanism to the impression cylinder, which presses it against the rotating blanket so that the inked image is transferred once again, this time to the final copy medium.

Water or Dampening System

One of the most critical features in offset printing is the correct balance between the quantities of dampening fluid and ink. To achieve this it is essential to have an accurate control of both systems and the first stage in setting the balance is to start with a minimum of dampening.

There are two methods of dampening, the conventional method applies dampening fluid directly to the plate whilst an alternative method, used on many office offset machines, applies fountain solution to the plate via the inking rollers. The latter arrangement enables some simplification of machine design in combining the inking and dampening operation and reducing the number of rollers.

In conventional dampening a train of rollers, usually four or five, carry the fluid from the dampener fountain to the surface of the plate. The rollers which contact the plate are covered with absorbent cloth which requires replacing periodically. They are moistened and driven by an oscillating roller made of corrosion resistant metal. This is supplied with moisture by another cloth-covered vibrator roller which has a make and break action with the oscillator and fountain rollers.

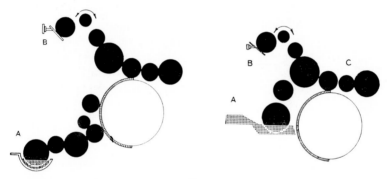

DIRECT DAMPENING AND COMBINED INKING AND DAMPENING
SYSTEMS
A. Water. B. Ink. C. Mixed ink and water.

There are various methods of controlling the flow of liquid to the vibrating cloth roller but the usual system employs a pawl and ratchet device which, according to setting, regulates the amount of rotation of the feed roller per revolution of the machine. It is important that the rollers are correctly set and well maintained. Solutions used will usually be as recommended by the machine manufacturer. Although dampening fluids are mainly water, proprietary brands include essential agents in correct proportions to eliminate many of the ink and water balance problems which puzzle the unskilled operator when they occur.

In the combined inking and dampening system there are normally only two dampening rollers, the fountain roller and pick-up roller.

The latter feeds a controlled amount of fountain solution to an intermediate roller of the inking train and from thereon dampening and inking are simultaneous functions of the single train of rollers terminating on the plate cylinder. The dampening fluid specially formulated for this system is recommended for easiest trouble-free working, although normal litho solutions can be used. The system is still regarded as somewhat unorthodox and in theory the presence of moisture in the inking system is bound to degrade the quality to a certain extent. However, with a correct choice of ink to suit the system, no reprographer is likely to be dissatisfied with the quality of duplicating obtainable and the popularity of machines of this type proves the point.

Inking System

On the conventional office offset duplicator, ink is drawn from an ink fountain and carried to the printing plate via a series of ink rollers. Local control of the volume of ink picked up from the fountain by the fountain roller is by adjustment of a series of thumbscrews which push against a thin wiper blade. Overall control of ink flow is

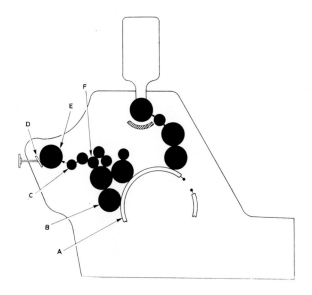

INKING SYSTEM

A. Plate cylinder. B. Ink forme rollers. C. Ductor roller. D. Ink fountain.
E. Fountain roller. F. Distributor, intermediate and vibrator rollers.

108

by pawl and ratchet adjustment of the speed of the fountain roller. The ductor roller rocks back and forth between the fountain roller and the first distributor roller. From hereon a series of distributor, intermediate and oscillating rollers, break down the ink into a thin workable film. The number of rollers varies according to type of machine.

Finally the ink is applied to the printing plate via the ink forme rollers, of which there may be one or two according to machine type. These forme rollers must be truly cylindrical. They consist of a metal core covered with a resilient rubber-like compound having the necessary hard wearing and chemical resisting properties.

Inking rollers must always be well adjusted and maintained in true and clean condition, free of glaze, low and high spots. The forme rollers in particular need regular checking in accordance with the manufacturer's instructions, both as regards condition and pressure of contact with the plate cylinder.

Printing Cylinders

Offset duplicators have three main cylinders. One supports the printing plate, another the blanket and the third is the impression cylinder which presses the paper against the blanket in the printing operation. Pressure adjustments are an important feature of this system. They are ink forme rollers and dampening roller to plate cylinder; plate cylinder to blanket cylinder and blanket cylinder to impression cylinder. Each adjustment involves a check for equality of pressure over the width of the cylinder. The maker's handbook should be consulted for the correct order of adjustments.

There is a design of machine which uses only two printing cylinders. A single large cylinder performs the functions of both plate cylinder and impression cylinder. While a master is being inked up on one segment of the cylinder, the other segment is pressing a sheet of paper against the blanket cylinder containing an image transferred from the master during the previous half-rotation. By introducing metal or rubber type into the impression segment and using the inking system but not the dampening system for this, both sides of the copy paper can be printed at the same time. The impression segment can also be used for embossing, scoring, perforating and direct lithography.

On the conventional three cylinder machines special arrangements can also be made to carry out selective printing, two colour printing simultaneously, and such mechanical actions as perforating, slitting and scoring of copies.

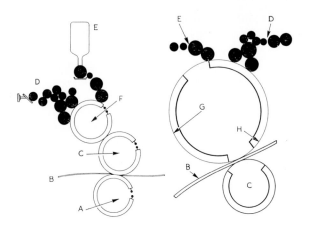

THREE-CYLINDER AND TWO-CYLINDER SYSTEMS

A. Impression cylinder. B. Paper. C. Blanket cylinder. D. Inking
system. E. Dampening system. F. Plate cylinder. G. Impression.
H. Plate.

Manufacturers are usually able to supply many additional or
alternative features to standard machines to suit specific requirements. Amongst these are automatic blanket cleaning, automatic
desensitizer applicators, numbering attachments, alternative master
clamps, and auxiliary rollers for the inking and dampening systems.

Paper Feeding Mechanism

The first step towards good duplicating begins with the mechanics
of feeding the paper accurately, one sheet at a time. According to the
class of offset duplicator used, the system may be a simple form of
friction feed similar to that used on stencil and spirit duplicators, or a
quite complex system of air suction pick up feet, rollers, belts and
grippers.

An example of the friction feed system is that incorporated in the
Rotaprint R.75. It operates automatically by means of the feeler bar,
the scraper bar and the intake rollers. The paper is gripped by the
feeler bar, is buckled by the backward movement of the scraper bar,
and then released by the feeler bar to be moved forward by the scraper
bar into the intake rollers. The feeler bar also controls the automatic
raising of the feed stack platform.

110

Machines with the more efficient air blower and suction feed are naturally more expensive but perform more exacting colour printing work as well as ordinary black and white duplicating.

There are many optional attachments to paper feed mechanisms offered by suppliers to cope with special problems. The Multilith 1250 class of offset duplicators have a particularly wide range of auxiliary attachments, some of the most useful being as follows:—

1. Auxiliary quick change card magazine taking paper down to 3″ × 5″ without disturbing feeder adjustments.

2. Auxiliary systems feeder chute which permits feeding of different sizes and weights of paper stock in succession without making any adjustments to the feeder.

3. Alternate sheet feed control which feeds one sheet with every two revolutions of the cylinder providing extra heavy ink coverage for certain types of work.

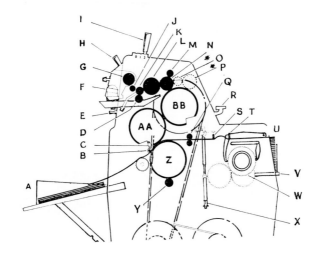

FRICTION PAPER FEEDING MECHANISM

A. Paper delivery. B. Delivery runners. C. Shoo-fly bar. D. Fount roller. E. Cylinder pressure adjustment lever. F. Fount reservoir. G. Ink duct roller. H. Ink duct lever. I. Ink lever. J. Ink vibrator roller. K. Distributing roller. L. Large distributing roller. M. Idling roller. N. Plate roller. O. Small oscillating roller. P. Plate roller. Q. Intake rollers. R. Paper feed key (Handle side) Cut-out key (Opposite). S. Scraper bar. T. Feeler bar. U. Paper feed. V. Stack platform. W. Stack raising gear. X. Scraper bar tension adjustment. Y. Drying roller. Z. C.P. Cylinder. AA. Blanket cylinder. BB. Plate cylinder.

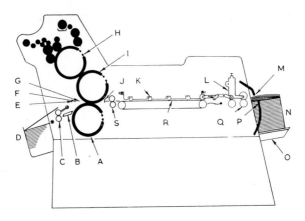

SUCTION PAPER FEEDING MECHANISM

A. Impression cylinder. B. Strippers separate paper from impression cylinder. C. Ejector wheels. D. Paper receiver and jogger. E. & F. Image transfers to paper and gripper fingers open. G. Gripper fingers on impression cylinder. H. Plate cylinder. I. Blanket cylinder. J. Halting stop fingers. K. Metal straps. L. Double sheet eliminator. M. Suction lifting feet. N. & O. Paper platform raised automatically. P. Paper separators and blowers. Q. Pullout rollers. R. Feed table transport tapes. S. Feed rollers.

4. Variable sheet quantity control, an electrical device attached to (2) which allows sheets from the chute to by-pass the automatic counter when extra copies in selected cases are required.
5. Side by side feeding attachment for feeding tabulator cards, envelopes, etc.
6. Paper feed control, enables the operator to easily control the exact number of sheets to be duplicated.
7. Vacuum booster to give extra lift for card stock from a pre-collated set of lighter weight material.
8. Right and left hand jogging attachments to ensure uniform alignment of each margin.
9. Multiple position guides, allow a positive jog of varying widths of paper stock across the throat of the register board.
10. Spring loaded pick-up rollers, recommended where a large variety of sheet sizes are to be duplicated for close register work.
11. Chain delivery to give positive gripper control for delivery of a sheet from the impression cylinder grippers to the receiver stack.

12. Perforating, numbering, scoring, signature and slitting attachments.
13. Features enabling the whole sequence of duplicating operations to be programmed and performed automatically.

Paper Stocks for Litho Duplicating

Although not every type of paper can be used in offset printing, the scope is much wider than is the case with spirit and stencil duplicating.

The selection and handling of paper is a matter requiring considerable experience and care. Papers with a dusty surface or loose fibres are quite unsuitable as the loose particles adhere to some extent to the rubber blanket and when they are transferred to the pressure rollers and inking device, degrading of ink and smearing occurs.

A capable operator can deal with papers from airmail weight up to lightweight cover and index boards provided surfaces are suitable. Tracing paper, cloths and films can also be handled on machines equipped with conventional inking if a suitable grade of ink is used.

Paper should never be placed on edge but always laid flat in store. Before the paper is used it should be kept for a few days in an atmosphere similar to that of the printing room. It is advisable to keep a thermometer and hygrometer in both printing room and stores in order to control temperature and humidity. The best conditions are a temperature of 20°C and 65 per cent humidity.

It is important that paper is fed to the machine in the correct running direction, particularly when accurate registration of image is important. Paper tends to curl around the axis of the grain or running direction and in cases where paper is badly stored this is often apparent as soon as a packet is opened by the curl already developed. However, paper should be flat when used and a simple test to ascertain running direction is to cut a piece the size of a postcard, moisten it and lay it flat on the hand; the paper will curl, and this will reveal the correct running direction.

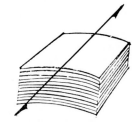

PAPER RUNNING DIRECTION

"Knocking up" of paper is another essential step to smooth machine running. Cut sheets of paper during guillotining and packing are tightly compressed but for easy machine feeding each sheet should be separated from its neighbours by a cushion of air. This is achieved by slapping the packet of paper, after un-wrapping, sharply on the edge of a bench to break any bonding of edges caused by guillotining, and then fanning out the sheets at both ends to allow air penetration. Alternatively a mechanical jogger can be used.

Another obvious point, but one sometimes overlooked by the operator, is that most materials have a right and wrong side on which to print. On a watermarked paper there will be no difficulty in recognising the right side but if there is any doubt, most materials are packed with the correct side uppermost.

TYPES OF PAPER AND BOARDS IN COMMON USE

Type	Substance (grams per sq. metre)	Remarks
Airmail	27–45	Thin, moderately strong, capable of numerous typed copies, will take typescript both sides for air letters.
Bank	45–60	Lightweight papers, used where lesser numbers of carbon copies required.
Bond	63–98	General-purpose paper for typing and manuscript work.
Duplicator	73	Semi-absorbent for use on stencil type duplicating machines.
Spirit Duplicator	63–89	Used on spirit duplicating machines. Smooth finish essential.
N.C.R. (no carbon required):		
Paper	49–81	General-purpose papers and boards which
Board	170–240	take copies without use of carbon paper.
Ledger	86–158	Strong papers, good writing surface used for account forms and ledgers.
Cartridge	102–170	Heavyweight paper for general typing and manuscript work.
Index Board	148–296	Strong with good rigidity for card-index systems and accounting machines.
Pulp Boards	185–288	Less strong than Index Boards, suitable for postcards, index and record cards, etc.
Ivory Boards	267–394	Thick, rigid board, matt and smooth finishes, suitable for visiting cards, menus, etc.
Manilla	180–320	Strong and durable, used for folders, job cards, tags, factory forms, etc.

The measurement, grams per square metre, is a useful unit of weight by area, which applies to all papers.

Offset Litho Duplicating Machines

It is extremely difficult to arrange offset litho machines into any functional grouping system. One might think that offset duplicators fall naturally into one group and offset printing machines into another. However, some of the most popular machines used in the

(*Top left*) Rex-Rotary 1500

Combined inking/damping. Quick colour change. Variable speed to 4800 i.p.h. Max. sh. size 10·2″ × 14·2″.

(*Top right*) Rotaprint R9/75. QC.

Fscp. friction feed short run systems duplicator, with automated features. Variable 2500 to 5000 i.p.h. Combined sh. size 13½″ × 9″.
Rex-Rotary 1500

(*Middle*) Multilith 1250

High speed machine. Vacuum feed 10 inking and 4 dampening rollers. Optional automating features. Up to 9000 i.p.h. Max. sh. size 11″ × 17″.
Rotaprint R95/2C

(*Bottom*) Rotaprint R95/2C

Dual inking system and twin plate cylinders simultaneously printing 2 colours in register. Max. sh. size 13½″ × 20″.

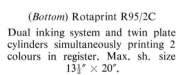

SOME OFFSET LITHO DUPLICATORS

office as duplicators are also just as popular in the printing department for long run and even colour printing. Copy size might, at one time have been used as a demarcation feature between printing and duplicating but cheap electro photographic masters prepared from drawing microfilm, has led to the development of the big sheet quick change litho duplicator. This is economic in the production of a

(*Top left*) A. B. Dick 325B

Single lever control table model systems duplicator. Automatic master loading and ejection.

(*Top right*) Rotaprint R30/CS

Special machine for printing continuous stationery.

(*Middle*) Gestetner 201S

Automatic control systems duplicator. Preset control of all systems throughout the printing cycle. Range of optional attachments. Converts instantly to long run duplicating.

(*Bottom*) Multilith 2550

Automatic sequence control duplicator. Programme facilities enable operator to attend two machines. Consistent high quality not dependent on operator skill. Automatic copy sorter can be fitted.

SOME OFFICE SYSTEMS OFFSET DUPLICATORS

(*Top left*) Rotaprint R17/85

Offers high quality printing and duplicating in large sheet sizes up to $13\frac{1}{2}'' \times 17\frac{1}{2}''$ at relatively low cost.

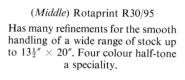

(*Top right*) A. B. Dick M.321

Easily operated general purpose table top duplicator. Nine roller inking system and two forme rollers.

(*Middle*) Rotaprint R30/95

Has many refinements for the smooth handling of a wide range of stock up to $13\frac{1}{2}'' \times 20''$. Four colour half-tone a speciality.

(*Bottom*) Multilith 1850

For sheet sizes up to $18'' \times 15''$ but as versatile and simple to operate as the popular 1250.

SOME NEWLY INTRODUCED OFFSET DUPLICATORS

dozen drawing prints and equally efficient in producing high class print in quantity from metal plates.

To attempt any grouping by mechanical features is equally un-rewarding owing to the flexibility introduced by the use of auxiliary attachments the groupings made here, therefore, are somewhat arbitrary and some overlap is inevitable.

CHAPTER XI

PREPARATION OF OFFSET LITHO MASTERS

The offset litho duplicating process is particularly well served in techniques developed for the preparation of cheap paper, plastic and metal masters. Many of these techniques are based on photography, which is a subject outside the scope of this manual. However, to appreciate the extent of the applications of offset duplicating it is necessary to know something of the general characteristics of the principal master-making techniques.

It may seem obvious that the correct master-making method for each particular job should be that which provides the cheapest master capable of providing the necessary number of copies of acceptable quality. However, it is not always quite so simple. It is likely that all the methods will not be readily available and even if they are, the cheapest may not be the quickest.

Another consideration which must be taken into account is achievement of standardised presentation in some fields of use of copy. A lengthy report containing well produced half tones and line drawings should not be spoilt by inclusion of textual copy bearing background soiling which is often typical of the use of the cheaper range of paper masters.

Direct Imaged Litho Masters

When the duplicating method is known before a document is prepared, it is always cheapest to prepare it directly on appropriate master material. In the case of offset litho duplicating, this material will be litho master sheets in one of the paper or plastic grades according to the number of copies required. The cheaper grades of master material are usually satisfactory for short runs of less than a hundred copies whereas the better quality types range from those giving hundreds of copies to those capable of producing many thousands.

The grade of master chosen is not the only limiting feature to the length of run obtained. Much also depends on the nature of the

118

image and for a typed image it is essential that a litho process ribbon is used. Here again, there are several grades and their purposes have been described in Chapter VI.

Another relevant feature is the degree of force applied by the typist to her keys. If a manual typewriter is used, the same natural stroke as when typing on ordinary paper should be used. With an electric typewriter the pressure should be adjusted to a key pressure setting low enough merely to deposit the character image on the surface of the master. Applying too heavy a pressure is a serious fault resulting in "hollow" characters in the copy.

The explanation for this is as follows. With a normal touch the typing lies on the surface of the master and produces an even fully-formed image. When the master is placed on the duplicator, ink builds up the image in an even manner to reproduce clear clean copies. If the typing action is extra hard (ostensibly to get good black copy) the typing is indented or "impressed" into the surface of the master. When the ink roller of the duplicator passes over the surface the roller makes contact only with the edge of each letter. Hardly any ink is deposited in the centre, and as a result you get only light outlines of a letter.

Writing or drawing on paper masters is as easy as on ordinary paper but, as in the case of typewriter ribbons, specially formulated pencil crayons and ball point pens are available. Once again the rule is, "Don't press too hard".

In addition to the litho reproducing pencils there is also a non-reproducing pencil. It creates an image on the master which does not reproduce on the copies and it is therefore useful for drawing guide lines on the master.

When preparing direct-imaged masters it is important to position the image correctly on the master. Otherwise the duplicating machine operator will waste a considerable amount of time in adjusting the machine to ensure correct positioning of the image on the copy paper. To assist in this direction, the masters are available bearing non-reproducing vertical and horizontal scales in typewriter standard spacings. This preprinting is usually lilac in colour and it enables the user to place the information accurately in the proper location on the master.

When the copies from a master are required to be printed upon a standard stationery form or letterhead, it is cheaper and more convenient to use reproducing pre-printed masters bearing the appropriate format. Plain paper can be used for the copy paper instead of printed stationery and no problem of registration arises. Stocks of these pre-printed masters can be prepared on an offset litho machine using plain master material provided a suitable ink is used and sufficient drying time allowed. Information can be added to the pre-printed master in just the same way as with blank masters, by typewriter, pencil or pen.

Masters are also often supplied as part of a carbon set. Usually the master is in the front position (the top sheet), but occasionally, it may be placed in the second position. When the masters are used in this way, they usually have a form printed on them. The master is used to duplicate the additional copies required whilst the carbon copies are for "immediate action" use.

Correcting Paper Masters

The most common source of trouble in preparing paper offset masters is in making corrections. The tendency is to erase an unwanted image completely. This is unnecessary and damages the surface of the master. Only the greasy surface of the image needs to be removed and this can be done most satisfactorily with a soft rubber using a light lifting stroke. Ordinary typewriter or ink erasers should not be used because they may contain abrasive substances which will smudge or damage the master. When typing in the correction over the erased area any tendency to apply extra pressure should be avoided.

Handling and Storage

One other important point is that paper masters should be handled with care both in preparation, and at all times before being mounted on the printing machine. Unlike the stencil and spirit processes, with the offset process the copy image is printed from the front of the master and any blemishes thereon which interfere with the hydrophilic nature of the surface will ink up during printing and spoil the copies. Therefore care should be taken to avoid finger marking by always handling the master by the edges and, for the same reason folding or creasing the masters should be avoided.

After printing, and providing the first printing has not exhausted the life of the image, paper masters can be stored for re-use if surplus ink is removed and the surface preserved by application of the recommended solution. The preservative is removed automatically by the process of etching at the re-run stage.

Masters by Photo-Copy Processes

It is now possible to make reasonably cheap offset masters from existing documents by several of the office photocopying processes, e.g. diffusion transfer, gelatine transfer, thermal, electrostatic and diazo processes.

Masters Prepared by Electrophotography

There are at present two forms of electrophotography in common use for the preparation of offset litho masters. One of these, and the first to be applied to this purpose, is the indirect process known as Xerography. It produces an image on plain master material, not directly from an original but indirectly by transfer from a photo-conductive plate. The second form is the direct process in which the photo-conductive layer is coated on the master or copy material and the image is formed directly upon this by exposure to the original.

Electrophotography is a subject requiring more extensive coverage than is possible in this manual but, in view of the importance of the process in the duplicating field, a brief explanation of its characteristics is necessary at this stage.

The principles are most easily understood if we consider how they are applied in their simplest form to the earliest platemaking equipment by the Haloid Co. using the indirect method. The equipment, still widely used, is known as the Xerox 1385 and consists of a camera, plate processing unit and image fusing unit.

A high rate of production of masters (usually in excess of 100 per day) from typed or drawn originals can be maintained. The master material is the same as for direct image work, the appropriate grade being chosen according to the number of copies required. The process is not well suited for producing masters from continuous or half tone subjects, or those containing solid image areas.

The process utilises the physical characteristics of selenium which will hold an electrostatic charge in the dark and release the charge to an earthing substrate in areas exposed to light. A sheet of aluminium coated with selenium is charged with electrostatic in the processor unit, loaded in a dark slide and exposed in the camera back in the same way as conventional film.

The plate in its dark slide is then inserted in the processor, the light shield removed, and the image developed by cascading micronised powder over the plate. The powder is attracted to the image

121

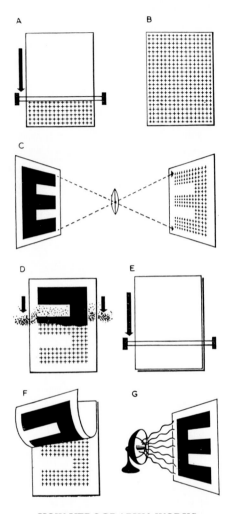

HOW XEROGRAPHY WORKS

A. Surface of specially coated plate is being electrically charged as it passes under wires. B. Shows coating of plate charged with positive electricity. C. Copy (E) is projected through lens in camera. Plus marks show projected image with positive charges. Positive charges disappear in areas exposed to light as shown by white space. D. A negatively charged powder adheres to positively charged image. E. After powder treatment (D) a sheet of paper is placed over plate and receives positive charge. F. Positively charged paper attracts powder from plate forming direct positive image. G. Print is heated for a few seconds to fuse powder and form permanent print.

area which still retains its static charge. The plate can then be viewed and surplus powder dusted off.

A paper offset master is then given an electrostatic charge in the processor in contact with the plate. The image is thus transferred from plate to master and at this stage is still in loose powder form and any unwanted portions of image can be wiped off. Permanent fixing is carried out by insertion in the fuser unit and a powdered resin component of the developer powder permanently fixes the image to the master by exposure to heat or alternatively to vapour according to the type of fusing unit employed.

Each selenium plate can be used for approximately 1000 exposures and in practice, six plates are housed in the processor unit and used in sequence since each plate needs a rest period of 10 minutes between exposures.

The later automatic Xerox office copying machines, using rotating selenium drums instead of flat plates, can also be used to create litho masters but since they deliver a copy with the image already fused, cleaning up of the copy by dusting off unwanted powder is not possible. A Xerox imaged paper master provides a harder wearing image than a direct typed master and therefore provides longer runs.

The direct method of electrophotography now marketed under a number of trade names, uses a photoconductive layer coated on the copy medium. Zinc oxide is the principle constituent of the coating. There are two methods of developing the image. In one, the toner is applied in dry-powder form and in the other, it is applied in liquid suspension. So far, copies prepared by the liquid toner method have not proved satisfactory as litho masters.

Normal office copies produced by the dry-toned process can themselves be used as short run offset duplicating masters. This is an important development in the offset duplicating field as it reduces the cost of a photo master very considerably.

In addition, there is a zinc oxide coated Multilith paper master available for use when better quality and longer duplicating runs are required. This master is also very cheap, costing little more than a short-run, direct-image master, but providing well over 1,000 good quality litho prints, The standard zinc oxide copy paper master is limited to about 100 litho prints.

Another advantage of the direct electrophotographic process is that it reproduces half-tones and solid image areas extremely well.

Photo-direct Production of Offset Masters

Only a little over two years ago Kodak introduced a completely new offset litho paper master material. Positive working, with a lith-type sensitised coating of projection speed based on silver halide, it has a capability of extended runs of at least 5000.

Since then a variety of automatic cameras and processors have become available for use with this material. Considering the high initial cost of the equipment, it is surprising how rapidly and how extensively the process has penetrated this highly competitive field. The explanation lies in the speed of production and quality of master facilitated by well designed equipment in combination with the silver sensitised emulsion. It would not be economic for the small user but it is claimed that a break-even point would be an output of about 150 plates a week. Some machines have a capability of over 500 masters per day with only one operator. Using the indirect electro-static plate making equipment, an output of 200 masters a day usually needs two operators.

Photo-direct masters do have some slight disadvantages. Reproduction of half-tones is by no means perfect although from coarse screens the results are satisfactory. They do not reproduce all colours although the range of sensitivity is fairly wide. Running conditions for photo-direct masters require certain techniques which are sometimes at variance with conventional offset methods. In other words, they are not compatible in use with other types of master on the same machine. However, providing a machine is set up with inking and running conditions exclusively for photo-direct masters, then little trouble should be experienced.

There are two ranges of equipment available for the preparation of photo-direct litho masters. One is the Itek range marketed in Britain by Kodak Ltd. under the trade name of Itek Platemaster. There are three camera/processor units offered, the 10.15, 11.17 and 20.24. The numbers represent the maximum size in inches of the offset plate that can be made on the unit. The camera is fitted with a prism to ensure right-reading copies and a reasonable degree of reduction or enlargement is provided. Focusing is motor driven and automatic.

The Verilith developer-incorporated plate material, is daylight loaded in roll form. It is cut to the desired length and fed by rollers through activator and stop solutions after exposure. A production rate of two plates per minute can be obtained.

The second range of equipment is marketed by Addressograph Multigraph Ltd. and uses the same projection speed plate material but in cut sheet form. The AM705 camera processor is a fully automatic unit making plates up to 11 in. by 18½ in. size. It has a 200 per cent linear enlargement facility down to 50 per cent linear reduction. The MTD 10 camera employs a separate loader processor and makes plates up to 10 in. by 16½ in. The MTD 30 camera, also using a separate loader processor, is a larger model accommodating plate sizes up to 15¾ in. by 19½ in.

In addition to these established A-M Photo-Direct cameras, two later models are suitable for same-size work up to 18 by 15 in. or 30 per cent reductions. The model 1070 camera works in conjunction with the A-M darkroom process or model 405P but the CLPA-3 is a semi-automatic model with a processor linked to the camera. Operating in daylight, the processor has a transport mechanism which takes a master from the magazine, positions it for exposure and then feeds it into the developer unit where processing is completed at a speed of 1½ minutes per master.

Diazo Sensitised Offset Masters

Diazo coatings provide positive images from positive originals and this makes diazo sensitised offset masters very useful for contact printing directly from originals when available in sufficiently translucent form. They are usually exposed in a vacuum printing down frame or alternatively, in dyeline copiers of suitable type.

To avoid loss of image quality, it is often worth-while preparing a laterally reversed diazo film intermediate for use in printing down the image on to the presensitised master. The film image will then be in direct contact with the sensitised surface of the plate, thus preventing undercutting of the image by refracted light rays which may be troublesome when the thickness of the base material separates the image from the sensitised surface. Ozatype Process film is a valuable material for this type of work.

Projection diazo masters are now available which may be used to create litho plates from microfilm.

125

CHAPTER XII

THE DIAZO PROCESS IN OFFICE SYSTEMS

Diazo, or dyeline, is a photo process and it is not related to office duplicating processes except by similarity of function. Nevertheless, when considering the field of application of duplicating processes, we must take into account the fact that the diazo process takes an ever-growing share of the office systems copying business. This is in spite of the flood of new processes and high speed duplicating machinery released to industry in recent years.

The reason is not far to seek. Diazo is still the most versatile and simplest of processes. It is also the most economic when only a limited number of copies is required. Its one disadvantage is that the original must have some degree of translucency although this is not such a limitation as it may seem since most office papers are translucent by diazo standards. In fact translucent paper can be supplied in various thicknesses from ordinary lightweight paper to comparatively stout card substance. In any case, practically all types of office copier will produce suitable translucent intermediates from the most opaque originals for quick and cheap diazo printing.

No other process offers such facilities for easy introduction of colour into everyday copying tasks. Variations of line colour are provided in the coating and in the developer, and there is a useful range of coloured base stocks. The flexibility of alterable diazo translucent and transparent intermediates is the very heart of enormous fields of application in office systems such as order-invoice, purchase order receiving, production control, etc.

These translucent materials are usually prepared with the image in reverse, i.e. printed with the coated side in direct contact with the subject matter on the original. This provides a sharper and stronger diazo image by eliminating the undercutting action of light rays passing through the thickness of the base material of the original. There is no inconvenience in viewing the image through the base of the translucent intermediate prepared in this way. Additional information can be added to the side opposite to that bearing the diazo image and subsequent prints will provide an overall quality of reproduction from the diazo image and newly added information which would not be attainable from an intermediate with a right reading image.

In the preparation of reports and specifications modern high speed printers have done a great deal to close the gap between diazo and the offset litho duplicator. There are some diazo printers on which it is possible to make a sixty page collated set of specification sheets ready for binding in no more than a minute.

To appreciate the useful applications of the diazo process in office copying, it will not be necessary for the student to have extensive technical knowledge but some understanding of the chemistry involved will be helpful.

How Diazo Works

The underlying principle of the diazo process is the use of two separate halves of an azo dyestuff which, under certain conditions of development will combine to give a coloured image. One of the halves of the azo dyestuff consists of a diazo compound which is sensitive to light, and which when exposed to light is changed so that it can no longer form a dyestuff with the other half. This other half is commonly referred to as the coupler and is designated blue coupler, yellow coupler, etc., according to which colour it forms with the diazo compounds.

Using the same basic principle, there are three distinct variations of the process, each using a different method of development but all producing a positive print from a positive original.

In the ammonia process both the diazo compound and coupler are combined in the coating of the base material, with stabilisers added to prevent premature coupling. At the development stage the stabilisers are neutralised by the ammonia vapour, and full development – or coupling – takes place.

In the semi-dry process only the diazo compound is coated on the base material, and the coupling chemical is the basis of the liquid developer which is applied, after exposure, to complete the printing process.

In the heat-developed process the coupler is incorporated in the coating mixture together with another chemical which liberates an alkali by the effects of heat.

In all cases the coating mixture is made acid to ensure stability of

127

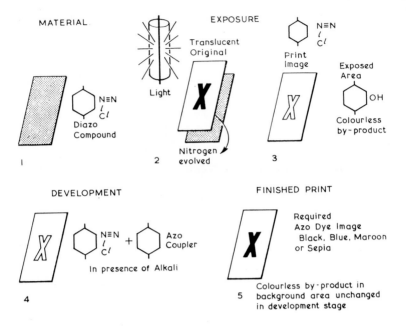

MATERIAL

EXPOSURE

Translucent
Original

Light

Diazo
Compound

Nitrogen
evolved

1

2

Print
Image

Exposed
Area

Colourless
by-product

3

DEVELOPMENT

FINISHED PRINT

Azo
Coupler

In presence of Alkali

4

Required
Azo Dye Image
Black, Blue, Maroon
or Sepia

Colourless by-product in
background area unchanged
in development stage

5

STEPS IN CREATING THE DIAZO IMAGE

(1) Material coated with light sensitive diazo compound.
(2) Translucent original placed above diazo material restricts passage
of light rays through image X. Action of light in unimpeded areas
decomposes the diazo compound by release of nitrogen.
(3) Pale yellow active diazo compound image remains in a background
of colourless non-active decomposition product (phenol).
(4) The azo coupler is allowed to combine with the diazo compound
image by creating an alkaline environment in the development stage.
(5) The colour of image of the finished print will be dependent on the
nature of the azo coupler used.

the diazo, and other additions are made to the basic chemicals to
refine the behaviour of the coated material in specific ways.

A choice of which form of diazo to use in office systems work
depends on the intended location and other environment circumstances. Each has advantages and disadvantages and some of these
are indicated in the table on page 130.

Nature of Original

As previously stated, diazoprinting requires a translucent original
and the ideal is one which allows the maximum light to pass through

the material where no lines (the subject matter) are present, while the lines themselves have the best light-stopping properties. It is the strength of the line and its relation to the background through which the light must pass which bears most on the time for which any given diazo paper should be exposed to light, and, consequently, the speed of printing.

It follows that the resultant print is dependent on the difference between the opacity of the base material and that of the line plus the opacity of the base. Where the lines are weak and the base material is opaque, it is not possible to allow sufficient light to pass through the original to convert all the diazo compound without some light passing through the lines themselves and affecting the compound underneath. As a result, undecomposed diazo compound remains generally on the print, and on development, gives a certain amount of background colour. Any attempt to remove this background by extra exposure affects the line image quality. Thus the quality of the original in respect of translucency of base material and opacity of line is all important in obtaining best results from a given diazo material.

The increasing use of diazo in office systems developed a need for a paper with a fair degree of translucency combined with the

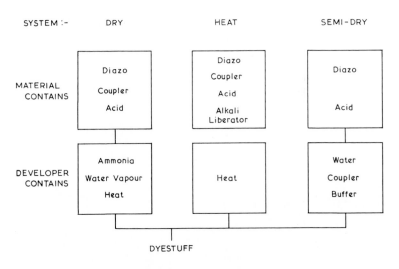

SYSTEM :-	DRY	HEAT	SEMI-DRY
MATERIAL CONTAINS	Diazo Coupler Acid	Diazo Coupler Acid Alkali Liberator	Diazo Acid
DEVELOPER CONTAINS	Ammonia Water Vapour Heat	Heat	Water Coupler Buffer

DYESTUFF

METHODS EMPLOYED IN EACH DIAZO SYSTEM
TO ACHIEVE A DYESTUFF IMAGE

ADVANTAGES AND DISADVANTAGES OF DIAZO SYSTEMS

Ammonia		Semi-dry		Heat-developed	
Advantages	Disadvantages	Advantages	Disadvantages	Advantages	Disadvantages
Dry prints	Fumes need ducting from site.	Can be sited anywhere	Prints slightly moist	Dryprints	Materials rather more expensive and limited in range; special storage conditions necessary to ensure reasonable shelf life.
Only routine developer maintenance required.	Not so easily relocated	Easily relocated / No warming up period for develop.	Developer has to be mixed	Easily moved. Simple operation	
No mixing of developer	Some residual ammonia odour.	No fumes	Developer unit requires daily cleaning	No chemicals	

appearance and feel of a good quality bond. This need has been filled by a new range of papers known as Diazobonds. They are manufactured to an approved specification, which guarantees that they are actinically translucent, to make them suitable as masters for diazo printing, while retaining the visual opacity of a good quality white bond paper. When used for internal forms, letterheadings, or carbon copies of letters, it ensures that copies can be made easily and cheaply at any time.

Producing the Translucent Master

Diffusion transfer, reflex, direct positive, stabilisation and electrostatic processes all return a higher copy cost than diazo. All are capable of producing translucent masters for diazo, given the use of the appropriate material. It follows, therefore, that wherever multiple copies are required from documents which are either double sided or too opaque for direct diazo reproduction, the more expensive processes should be used only for providing the intermediate. If the principle of producing all internally generated documentation on a diazobond or other actinically translucent material is adopted, the more expensive processes will only be required for single copies of incoming documentation or the production of a diazo master from such documents.

Any business machine capable of creating an opaque image on ordinary paper can create a translucency for diazo printing. For example, multipart form sets used in computers, tabulators, teletype machines, telex units, punch tape writing machines and typewriters can include a sheet of translucent paper which can be used for diazo printing. In some cases the multi-part form itself can be eliminated or the number of sheets in the set reduced by using a translucent top or second copy. Nearly all manual writing devices such as pencil and pen can be used to create a diazo master.

Any process capable of reproducing an opaque image can create a diazo original. This includes offset and stencil duplicators, but specifically excludes the hectographic process, which cannot produce an opaque image. These duplicating processes usually originate with a somewhat expensive master and require operator skill. While they can be more economical for runs over 10 copies, they are less so if a small number of further copies are required at a later stage, and the master must be treated for preservation. Diazo can implement these processes by the inclusion of a translucency as the last copy of the original duplicating run.

131

Diazo Printing Procedure

Diazo has the advantage of being a daylight process and the light energy required to print the coated materials must be relatively intense and rich in the "actinic blue" light, i.e. the blue to ultra violet band of the spectrum. High pressure mercury vapour discharge lamps provide this type of light energy and are now commonly used when a high printing speed is necessary. Low pressure mercury vapour fluorescent tubes with appropriate phosphor coatings, form very convenient sources but the light energy is limited and they are used only where lower printing speeds will suffice.

The printing machine must be designed to allow a maximum of light energy to reach the diazo coating as it passes around the light source. For this reason, discharge tubes of fused silica (quartz) are usually preferred and glass cylinders of Pyrex, or similar glass having low absorption of light in the blue to ultra violet waveband, are commonly used. The cylinder is arranged to rotate around the tubular UV light source, motivated by a set of endless bands which also conduct the original document and print paper around the cylinder. The original is positioned face up on the emulsion side of the diazo paper and fed forward on the bands, the curvature of the glass cylinder ensuring good contact during rotation around the light source.

After exposure the original is separated from the exposed diazo material, either manually or automatically according to the type of machine, and the print passed to the developing unit. For ammonia-developed materials this unit consists of a chamber charged with ammonia fumes and for the semi-dry variety, a series of rollers applies liquid developer to the surface of the print. For heat developed diazos, passage over a hot roller suffices.

The period of exposure to the light source is controlled by adjustment of the speed of traverse of the transport bands, although on some machines it is also possible to control the lamp output. Printing speed and developing speed are usually interlinked.

Some machines have been specially developed to provide a much higher print output than is possible by simple handfeeding of an original for each print. Mechanical retention of the original around the glass cylinder whilst a dialled number of prints is prepared from it, raises the output potential of the process very considerably. The linked systems of master changing, print developing and decollating must, of course, also be automated to keep pace with the input programme.

132

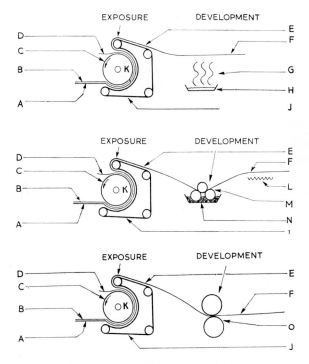

THE DIAZO PRINTING PROCESSES

Top: Ammonia development. *Middle:* Liquid development.
Bottom: Heat development.

A. Diazo paper coated side up. B. Original face up. C. Cylinder (rotating). D. Original. E. Exposed Diazo. F. Developed print. G. Ammonia vapour. H. Heating tray. J. Transport bands. K. Ultra-violet light. L. Dryer. M. Developer rollers. N. Developer. O. Heated rollers.

One desirable feature not yet universal is the automatic selection of correct exposures for each original. Attempts have been made to introduce this capability by means of photo electric cells but the high additional cost and limited demand has restricted its introduction. However, in office systems work the originals are usually of standard quality and frequent adjustment of exposure or printing speed is not required.

The diazo machine operator very quickly becomes adept at judging the printing speed required for each type of original. Incorrect setting of the speed control is immediately apparent by comparison as follows:

133

Overexposure (too slow)	weak dye lines pure white background
Underexposure (too fast)	strong dye lines heavily coloured background
Correct exposure	strong dye lines little or no trace of background colour

One of the most valuable features of the diazo process in office systems work is the facility it offers to create intermediate masters on which unwanted information may be erased and new information substituted or added. The translucent base materials available for this purpose are numerous and include tracing papers, tracing cloths, matt surfaced polyester films and clear foils. It is very important that these materials are correctly exposed in order to gain the maximum advantage from the line intensification characteristic which they possess. In the event of underexposure (too high a printing speed), the indicative background colouring is also intensified, making the print quite unsuitable for use as an intermediate master. Most intermediate diazo materials give a sepia coloured image as this provides the greatest opacity to ultra violet light during subsequent printing. Often it is possible to reproduce a diazo print of better line quality from a sepia line intermediate than could have been reproduced directly from the original.

Intermediate masters in clear film bearing standard information are often used as overlays on other originals to produce composite prints.

Diazo Machines

Machines for preparing drawing prints usually have a printing width in excess of 40 in. They can also be used for printing small documents at high speed but they need more floor area than is generally available in the office. The most usual feed widths of diazo office copying machines is in the 10 in. to 16 in. range. The simplest of these are only about the size of a typewriter and usually employ a few fluorescent tubes as the light source and roller development for semi-dry diazo materials. There is even a semi-automatic model available in this class, the Ilford Azoflex 161, which retains the original during a printing run until all the copies are printed at speeds of up to 700 an hour.

Other larger table top varieties are available with high pressure mercury vapour lamps, some with automatic separation of original from print after the exposure cycle. There is a preponderance of semi-dry machines in this and in the higher output range, due to the fact that installation of ammonia machines in offices has some complications in the ducting away of fumes. Machines for heat-developed diazo have not yet achieved the popularity of the semi-dry or ammonia versions.

In the free standing high output range there are some very highly sophisticated models specially developed for office systems work. Perhaps the most highly automated of these is the Azoflex 155 synchronised printing, developing and collating machine. It has an output potential of up to 4,000 quarto size prints per hour. The 155 automatically feeds in the original, runs off the number of copies programmed, cuts, develops, dries and collates them at the same time feeding in the next original to be printed. The machine will take rolls of print paper each 450 yards long, of various widths, and the exposing cylinder units are rapidly interchangeable to cater for originals of various lengths. The maximum size of print is $17\frac{1}{2}$ in. wide by 13 in. long.

There is a very wide range of office document diazo copiers, costing anything from £100 to £5000 and there are far too many models

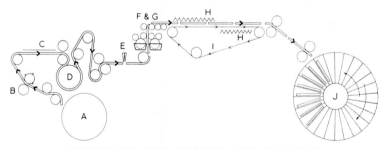

AZOFLEX 155 AUTO PRINTER AND COLLATOR

A. Reels of 400 to 600 yds. length according to weight of paper. B. Paper slitter for use when two smaller originals are printed side by side. C. Original placed on feed table and automatically fed. Required number of copies dialled. D. Exposing cylinder interchangeable for varying lengths of original. E. Paper guillotined into individual sheets. F & G. Microgrooved roller development. H. Heaters. I. Conveyor passes prints through drying section to collator. J. Prints fall one by one into consecutive compartments of the collator. Alternatively all prints can enter one compartment.

SOME OFFICE DOCUMENT DIAZO COPIERS

Make & Model	Feed	Max. Print Width	Development	At max. speed Qrto. copies per hour
B & A bandaprint	Semi-auto	11"	Semi-dry	2000
Ilford 161	Semi-auto	12"	"	700
Anson MR63	Single	18"	"	750
Ilford 135	Single	17"	"	1000
Hall Harding Triton	Auto-Roll	10"	"	1500
Ozalid Ozaminor III	Single	15"	Ammonia	1000
Bandathermal 14	Single	15"	Heat	1000
Ilford 4800	Auto-Roll	26"	Semi-dry	7000
Hall Harding GAF360	Auto 2 Roll	19"	Ammonia	5000
*Hall Harding GAF370	Auto-Roll	15"	"	4000
*Ilford Azomatic	Auto-Roll	18½"	Semi-dry	4000
Ilford 761	Semi-auto	11¾"	Heat	600

All the above machines provide automatic separation of original from copy before development.

* These machines handle unburst computer output.

136

within the range to consider them all here. However, those listed opposite do have up-to-date features which make them interesting examples of the present generation of equipment.

All the above machines provide automatic separation of original from copy before development.

Two most recently introduced diazo machines for office systems work are the GAF Antara 360 for ammonia developed materials and the Ilford Azoflex 761 for heat developed materials.

The GAF 360 incorporates solid state electronic controls. Two rolls of diazo stock are accommodated together, one may be 8 to 13 in. wide and the second 15 to 19 in. wide. The correct roll is automatically selected and fed, dependent upon the width of original presented, and then guillotined to match the length of original as it enters the printing head. The machine computes the precise exposure and sets the printing speed. There is an overriding manual control setting for underprint or overprint (background control) and also a manual control for alternative hand feeding of cut sheets of special materials. Maximum speeds may be up to 60 ft. per minute. An alternative version, the GAF370, is designed to handle unburst computer output.

The Azoflex 761 is a compact desk top machine using thermal diazo paper which requires no developing liquid or chemicals. No matter how many copies are required the original need only be fed into the machine once. A unique retention device holds the original until all the copies have been made. The sheets of diazo paper are automatically fed and the operator only needs to place the required number of sheets on the feed table. After exposure the original is automatically separated from the copy paper and copies are stacked at the front of the machine. In the automatic feed condition prints up to 11.8 in. wide and 14.6 in. long can be made. By switching to manual feed any reasonable length of paper can be printed. Speed is controlled manually and heat development is provided by two thermostatically controlled quartz infra-red elements.

CHAPTER XIII

NEW DUPLICATING PROCESSES

Adherography

There are several copying processes which, due to the high production rate made possible by automatic equipment, now compete in convenience at least, with the conventional office duplicating processes. One of these is the Adherography process which will produce copies from direct imaged or dual spectrum facsimile masters at 40 copies per minute.

The Minnesota Mining & Manufacturing Co. have developed the process and the equipment consists of a Model 74 Speed Copier and a Model 209 automatic dry photo copier employing the dual spectrum thermic process. The speed copier is the duplicator and this is offered on a hire basis plus charges for the number of copies metered.

The companion automatic dual spectrum Model 209 copier, which provides photo imaged masters for the Speed Copier, was first offered as part of a package deal with the Model 74 duplicator under the collective title of "System A-09". However, the Model 209 may now be installed independently on a straight hire basis (at present £11 per month) and this substantially reduces the cost of the facsimile duplicating masters for use on the Speed Copier. It also makes straight copying by the dual spectrum process more highly competitive in the office copying field.

The direct image Speed Copier masters are of light weight paper coated on the rear side. They can be imaged by direct typing or writing and may be litho printed with a stationery format for systems work. The prepared master is placed on the glass drum of the speed copier and the required number of copies dialled. Each master will produce up to 200 copies.

The printing operation can be likened to offset litho, except that it is much easier to operate and both master and copies are completely clean and perfectly dry. The copy paper used may be any ordinary bond paper. The method is to heat the master by infra-red as copy paper is fed to it. The heat softens the darker image areas of the master and, under pressure, a transfer of a tacky latent image is effected. The copy then moves into a developing unit where a carbon powder is cascaded over it in a manner similar to that employed in the electrostatic process. The powder sticks to the tacky image and this is fused into a permanent image as the copy passes through a heat fusing unit.

The machine requires no warming up period and no operator skill is necessary. However, it is a fairly complex piece of equipment and at present a fair amount of servicing by supplier seems to be necessary. This will no doubt be considerably reduced as experience is gained and the machine graduates to a higher stage of development.

All existing originals, even those in multi-colour, can also be "speed copied" by creating an intermediate facsimile master on the Model 209 copier.

Adherography prints are not as sharp as those from offset litho direct image masters, but they compare favourably with stencil or good dyeline copies.

Thermo-Fax Systems Copying

Thermo-Fax systems papers provide a useful method of short-run duplicating which can be employed in the following three broad areas of office documentation.

THE 3M MODEL 209 DRY PHOTOCOPIER (*left*)
AND MODEL 74 SPEED COPIER

1. Controlled copying. This covers a very wide range of copying applications when the preparation of the original is within the control of the user, and the number of copies required does not exceed 25.

2. Replacement of carbon paper. While there is some justification for typing up to four copies of a document using carbon paper, when more copies are required there is certainly a case for typing the original on a Thermo-Fax Type A master sheet and producing the required number of copies on systems copy papers.

3. Business forms. The process is widely used for the office copying requirements of order/invoicing and purchasing/receiving systems, etc.

The Thermo-Fax systems process falls short of being a real duplicating process by reason of the limited number of copies which can be prepared from a master. In performance and cost it can probably be compared with the diazo process. Convenience and cleanliness in operation are its most attractive features, especially when compared with spirit duplicating on short run work

The basis of the process is the Type A systems master paper. It is a lightweight paper coated on the back, which is insensitive to light and heat and remains perfectly dry and clean throughout the copy-making operation. The master may be prepared by any mechanical means, i.e. it may be pre-printed, typed or written upon, prepared by use of rubber stamps, carbon paper, etc. A Type A master sheet may be included in a carbon set. The image should be put on the front of the paper, the back, or coated side, being identified by an imprint.

There are two forms of copy paper, each in various colours and all coated on the front. Type B Systems copy paper is a bondweight paper available in four colours and white. Type S copy paper is a 40 per cent cheaper variety in eight colours but there is no pure white. The Type B paper provides a dark brown image and the type S, a dark grey-blue image.

The copies can be prepared on the standard Thermo-Fax infra-red office copiers but for high output applications an automatic machine, the Encore-Automatic, is available with a potential output of 25 copies per minute. As with the diazo process, the master is placed on top of the copy, both papers face up. They are hand fed when using a standard Thermo-Fax machine but with the Encore the master is clipped in the machine and paper feed is automatic.

Duplicating by Electrophotography

This newest form of duplicating is a development of xerography, the indirect electrostatic process. Based on the range of Rank Xerox office copiers, the new Rank Xerox 2400 copier/duplicator has broken into the duplicating field by its speed of operation—40 copies per minute or 2400 per hour. The machine is a very sophisticated piece of equipment and is the result of five years of development and an investment of many millions of dollars in research. Like other Rank Xerox copiers and copier/duplicators it is available on a rental basis with all charges based on meter readings. There is a minimum monthly charge of £125. The pricing is designed to suit runs of any length with a sharp price per copy reduction for runs of six copies or more.

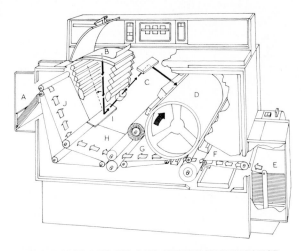

THE RANK XEROX 2400 COPIER/DUPLICATOR

1. The original document is placed face down upon the curved glass platen (B) where two banks of specially developed fluorescent lights illuminate it from below. The oscillating mirror (I) scans the document and reflects the image, sending it along the optical path through a lens to a fixed mirror (C). From there it is reflected onto the selenium-coated drum (D).
2. The paper on which copies are to be produced (E) is brought up to the proper level by an automatic elevator. It is fed into the machine and transported along belt (F).
3. At the first set of rollers, the sheet of paper is properly aligned before moving to the drum (D) where the image is transferred to it. Then it passes along belt (G) to the heated roll fuser (H) which permanently fixes the image into the paper's surface.
4. From that point, the paper is simply carried along transport (J) to the output tray (A) that will neatly stack up to 500 sheets. A unique vacuum system holds the paper securely to all three transport belts.

141

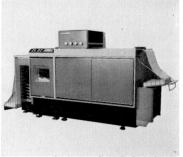

(*Top left*) Xerox 2400 Copier/Duplicator with linked automatic sorter.

(*Top right*) Xerox 2400 IV Computer Forms Duplicator.

(*Left*) Xerox 660 desk top copier.

RANK XEROX COPIER/DUPLICATING MACHINES

The whole concept of copier/duplicating is ease and simplicity of operation. No intermediate duplicating masters are required, no chemicals or inks to soil the hands and no machine adjustments. Only a dial to set for the required number of copies, a button to press and the prints flow at one every $1\frac{1}{2}$ seconds. For all this convenience it is not surprising that the prints cost a little more than those from conventional duplicating processes.

The principles of indirect electrophotography are briefly described in Chapter 10. The 2400 machine is designed to speed up and introduce a high degree of automation to each stage of the process. How this has been achieved is illustrated on page 141.

Xeroduplicator Construction

The machine requires a floor area of about 2 ft. 6 in. × 5 ft. 6 in. but access space is required on all sides. A 30 amp power circuit is necessary. The plain paper used should be of 80/85 g.s.m. substance and the machine can be set at any time to accommodate three sizes between 10 in. × 8 in. to 13 in. × 8.5 in. A lever, repositioned by the operator when changing the size of paper, sets the magazine to the selected size. To reload the magazine it is lowered to the charging position by press button.

The drum is larger than on the earlier Rank Xerox copiers, being designed to carry three copy images simultaneously. This is one of the features that has enabled a high copy speed to be achieved. It is 30 in. in circumference and 15.25 in. in length but the selenium coating extends to only 13.33 in. The copy platen itself is 14.25 in. by 8.75 in. and the original may be this size or larger, providing the image area does not exceed the stated limit of 13 in. × 8.5 in.

The platen is curved to conform with the arc of scanning performed by a mirror which oscillates below at a speed of 40 movements per minute. The optical scan cam is the component which rocks the mirror back and forth and to do this with sufficient accuracy the cam's tolerances require control of its measurements to within 17 millionths of an inch.

Illumination is provided by two banks of six high intensity fluorescent tubes coated internally with phosphor. To achieve the extremely long lamp life necessary without sacrificing luminous output, a close control of the temperature of the lamps has been introduced. Cool air is directed to the lamps and platen glass whilst the lamps are illuminated to prevent excessively high temperatures in this area.

Another serious problem arose in achieving high speed development of the electrostatic image. It was discovered that variations in humidity had serious effects in development. This was cured by adding a special electrode to the developer housing. The drum coating gives wide exposure latitude and colour response, and this obviates the need for any exposure control on the fixed aperture stationary lens. There are three stages in cleaning the image from the drum: (1) by corotron electrostatic reversal; (2) by vacuum and brushing by synthetic fibre brush; (3) electrical discharge by light. Periodic maintenance cleaning of the drum is unnecessary because of the elaborate built in automatic cleaning.

The image is attracted to the electrostatically charged paper in the usual way but refinements in techniques have reduced the quantity of toner used on each copy. The method of fusing the image to paper is entirely new. Instead of radiated heat, plastic coated rollers are used, the top one being heated internally by an infra red element. To ensure that deposits of toner do not build up on the hot roller, silicon lubricant is applied by a contact pad fed from a reservoir, which needs occasional topping up by the service engineer during routine maintenance procedures. This positive method of impressing the molten developer into the paper eliminates the troubles of dusting off of print image sometimes experienced with earlier machines.

The machine needs a warming-up period of 5–10 minutes and the first print of each original is delivered in 12 seconds. Further copies arrive at $1\frac{1}{2}$ second intervals. Pre-selector dials are located on the control panel which programme the machine to produce the required number of copies. Programming is achieved by an impulse generator which is linked to the copy track and this device also transmits information to two counting meters for billing purposes. The first meter records all copies made irrespective of the length of the copy run and the second records one count for each of the first five copies made during a single run. The meters therefore provide the user with a check on the number of copies run in each mode.

The 2400 copier/duplicator is visualised as a machine which will fill a need for fast convenient production of business systems copies in the short to medium run range. To compete with conventional duplicating methods for the longer runs, in which the per copy cost is considerably cheaper, its success will depend upon what value the user places on the convenience factor of this method of duplicating.

An optional extra for the 2400 copier/duplicator will be a linked automatic sorter that does away with hand-collating when copying multi-page documents. Speed of sorting is at the same rate as the machine – 2400 per hour.

Modular in construction, the sorter can be supplied in any number of 10-bin units between two and five, each bin having a capacity of 150 copies.

Before starting the copying or duplicating run, the operator selects the number of bins to be used. When collating complete sets as they are copied, the individual pages are inserted automatically in sequence in the bins according to the number of sets required.

For example, 60 copies of a 40-page report can be run off on the 2400 and collated ready for binding in an hour. All modules have a flat top to facilitate binding, stapling and stacking of finished sets.

Sorters will be rented with the 2400 copier/duplicator, the rental charge being dependent on the number of 10-bin modules installed.

Another version of the 2400 is the 2400 IV computer forms duplicator, automatically producing direct from the original forms as many copies as required on ordinary paper at the rate of 40 per minute. Every copy, from first to last, is sharp and clear with a very high degree of legibility. Use of single-ply stock forms saves the expense and inconvenience of multi-carbon-interleaved sets which also require separating and decollating. The original can be retained as a master set and additional copies can be made simply whenever needed, increasing computer utilisation and without affecting its routine.

Unwieldy 15 × 11 inch computer printout is automatically reduced to the more convenient A4 size ($11\frac{3}{4}$ × $8\frac{1}{4}$ inches) so that all reports are uniform and standard in size—which also simplifies binding, handling and filing which can be housed in standard cabinets. Further savings and convenience can be achieved by copying direct on to pre-punched paper. Smaller documents can be copied in the same size as the original, to give standard size output from different sizes of input.

The machine is simple to use. The concertina-forms are fed into the transport mechanism, the required number of copies set on the control panel and the machine start button is pressed.

A high-speed sorter automatically collates complete sets as they are copied. Supplied in 10-bin modules, up to three can be fitted to the machine, each bin having a capacity of 150 copies. Up to 30 sets of a 150-page report, involving 4,500 pages can, therefore, be copied to the reduced size, collated and ready for binding and distribution in under two hours. Extra copies of any particular page, such as a summary sheet, can be fed straight into a special 500-page capacity bin without interfering with the collation of the main report.

Users of the new system do not need to hold stocks of special pre-printed forms and can also save on programming and computer time. With the use of sets of simply prepared transparent overlays, (pre-printed with guide-lines, standard form headings, masking panels etc.), the copies of each report can be produced combining the printout on the forms with the overlay details. Sections of reports can, therefore, be highlighted or masked out to separate significant from irrelevant data, making the system a forms creator as well as a duplicator.

Rank Xerox have also raised the speed of two other electrostatic copiers to bring them into the copier/duplicator class.

The new push-button 660 desk top model now has a copying cycle of approximately 7 seconds, 520 prints per hour. It is intended to provide the quality and convenience of xerographic copying and duplicating at the point of need, on the desk.

The 660 copies onto ordinary paper up to $8\frac{1}{2} \times 13$ inches. As this machine is intended for use as a duplicator as well as a copier, the copies are same-size and no gripper marks are reproduced. Any copies from 1 to 15 can be dialled. For more than 15 copies, the dial is set to "Multiple" and the run length is automatically monitored on the built-in counter.

A new model of the 720 copier/duplicator enables increased speeds of up to 33-1/3 per cent to be achieved. It now has two operating speeds, its standard rate of 720 copies per hour and a choice of either 840, 870 or 960 copies per hour, depending on the setting of a new scanning device. The 720 speed is for a full length scan of paperwork from A4 (approx. $11\frac{3}{4}$ inches long) up to 14 inches. For smaller documents, according to the most common size used and chosen by each customer, the device is pre-set for a shorter scan with a corresponding increase in speed. Having made his choice, the machine is set to produce copies of documents $11\frac{3}{4}$ inches (A4) or 11 inches (American quarto), or 10 inches (Quarto) in length at the rate of 840, 870 or 960 per hour respectively. The customer selects his operating scan by the flick of a switch.

The very latest model from Rank Xerox is a machine which raises the speed of xerographic duplicating to 3600 copies per hour.

The 60-copies-per-minute machine, called the 3600 from its hourly output rate, is a direct development from the 2400 copier/duplicator. With its 50 per cent increase in speed, this machine further breaks down the barrier between office copying and short-run duplicating. Producing copies direct from original documents, the 3600 eliminates stencil or other master preparation as well as machine make-ready time. Declining-cost meters reduce the cost per copy according to length of run and total number of copies produced monthly.

A linked automatic sorter, similar to that described for the 2400, is also available for the 3600.

CHAPTER XIV

CHOOSING THE PROCESS

When the need arises to consider installing duplicating equipment, choosing the most suitable process involves careful consideration of a number of points. Some of these find a ready solution but other considerations are less clear cut and solutions vary according to the importance of the work involved, the special characteristics of potential processes and the nature of any existing equipment. There may even be some influential local prejudice, or objection by operators to certain processes, to be taken into account.

When in doubt as to the most suitable process for the type of work to be handled, it is often helpful to set out a questionnaire with the object of establishing all known facts about the type of original documents to be used and about copies needed. Such a questionnaire could be developed around the following.

Original Documents

1. *Is preparation of the original controlled within the duplicating area? If so can it be prepared as a duplicating master?*
   The cheapest and quickest method of making more than 5 copies is by a direct imaged master and the appropriate duplicating process, i.e. spirit, offset litho or stencil. When only a few copies are needed and perhaps more on future occasions, a translucent master for the diazo process would be economic and convenient.

2. *If not, is a master-making facility readily available? If so what type of master will it provide?*
   With an existing original, using an office copier to make an intermediate duplicating master, or translucent master, will still make the duplicated copies much more economically than by re-typing.

3. *Will the master be needed again in the future? If so will special storage conditions be required and available?*
   Spirit masters can be filed for re-use, but the number of copies

they will provide is limited. Inked stencils are not very conveniently stored. Litho paper masters can be stored but they should be depleted of ink and treated with a preserving solution after each run. This is worthwhile if long-run masters are used. Diazo masters are easiest to file but diazo prints are comparatively expensive for long runs.

4. *What will be the maximum size of original?*
Office photo copying and duplicating processes provide limited size of copy, usually up to foolscap. Brief size machines are available but are more expensive. Diazo is more flexible as to size of original to be copied.

5. *Will the subject matter be liable to alteration or correction?*
Additions are easy on any duplicating master but alteration is more tedious. Corrections are easiest to make on plain paper or translucent paper.

6. *Will the subject matter be typed, written or drawn, or a mixture of all three?*
Typing raises no problem on any master material but a litho ribbon is needed for litho and a black photo process ribbon gives best results on diazo translucent masters. Writing or drawing is easy on spirit, litho or diazo masters but special tools are needed for stencils. Reproduction ball points or pencils are satisfactory for litho or diazo. A mixture of subject matter, especially if half tones are included, can be reproduced most satisfactorily by the litho process.

7. *How many masters will need duplicating each day?*
Whichever process is chosen, the work load will decide the model of machine necessary.

Copies

8. *How many copies will usually be required?*
Will there be a percentage of the work needing less than five copies or more than 1000 *copies?*
This will affect the choice of process more than any other factor. Spirit is cheapest for short runs, stencil is satisfactory for intermediate runs and litho is the obvious choice for long runs. If there are a proportion of short and medium runs in addition to long runs, litho is economic for these too. For regular requirements of only a few copies, diazo may be considered. For only one or two copies from existing originals one must consider an

office photo copying process, although the copies are comparatively more expensive.

9. *Is office systems work envisaged?*
   If so, is line selection required?
   Will all the information on the master be needed on the copies or will some areas need to be suppressed automatically on some copies?
   For straightforward systems duplicating, spirit, litho or diazo are possible processes, but if more complex documentation is required spirit systems machines must be considered.

10. *Will the copies need to be on pre-printed stationery? If so could the format be included as a pre-print on the master?*
    The litho process offers an advantage in its facility to economically print any form of stationery and pre-print its own masters. It can also print a litho master or translucent master from a master. Spirit or stencil masters bearing pre-printed formats can be obtained from suppliers but these cannot economically be prepared internally.

11. *Will enlargement or reduction of the original be required?*
    Some form of optical equipment will be required to enlarge or reduce and if this is installed, offset litho would be the most compatible duplicating process.

12. *Will copies in multicolour or different coloured inks be required?*
    The spirit duplicating process will produce multicoloured copies cheaply and easily but if high quality copies are necessary the offset litho process is the obvious alternative.

13. *How permanent must the copies be?*
    There is some danger of spirit and diazo copies fading in adverse conditions. Stencil and litho copies can be considered permanent.

14. *What balance can be struck between quality and economy?*
    The quality of the finished copy is generally dependent upon its ultimate use. For copies of a temporary nature for internal use, legibility is usually all that is required, whereas documents to be used as permanent records or sent to other companies often justify the extra expense necessary to obtain the best quality work.

15. *What is the total volume of work likely to be required in one day?*
    The total quantity of work required per day should be con-

sidered from two aspects. The number of masters to be duplicated per day is the more important one because, on many duplicators, master changing takes up as much time, when short runs are involved, as actual running time. The total quantity of prints required per day is supplementary information to that on the number of masters involved and together they will indicate the most suitable process and range of machines to meet the requirement.

The list of answers to these questions will usually narrow the choice of process down to one or two. A further stage of investigation into the relative costs will probably make the final choice easy. This investigation must be thorough and it should take into account all items of cost including labour. Too often the customer accepts costs presented by the supplier which only include material and machine costs.

Costing

The first item to consider is the dispersal of machine costs over the number of copies to be made annually. These costs may be in depreciation over a number of years or in hire or leasing charges. Whichever arrangement is contemplated, the annual cost can be ascertained and to this must be added maintenance costs, perhaps in the form of a charge for a service contract. Electric power and floor area costs may also be included but these are not usually significant. The estimated annual output of copies set against the total machine costs establish the machine costs per copy.

It is not difficult to establish materials cost per copy but an allowance for wastage must be estimated and included.

Other consumables such as chemicals, inks, cleaners, etc., can be estimated from figures obtained from suppliers and converted to an annual figure to set against the annual output of copies.

Estimating labour costs is an exercise in which practical demonstrations prove helpful if they can be arranged with the suppliers of the machines in question. This affords opportunities to study and assess all the time consuming operations and the results assist in estimating the performance of the intended regular operator if and when a machine is installed.

To convert operating times for various lengths of run into labour costs per copy, the actual cost of the operator's time in producing copies must be established. This is not as simple as it appears at first sight. A machine operator working a $7\frac{1}{2}$ hour day occupies, on average, about 45 minutes of this in a non-productive way. Some of this lost time may be management approved but some will undoubtedly be frowned upon and occur nevertheless. About 20 per cent of the remaining time is spent on legitimate tasks associated with preparing copies but not in actually producing them, e.g. receiving, sorting and arranging work, machine and material preparation, recording and assembling of finished work, settling priorities and answering queries. The operator's whole cost, and this includes payments for sick absence, holidays, superannuation, etc., must be set against the time utilised in actually producing copies and in most cases an appropriate share of the sectional indirect labour cost will also be added. It will be found convenient to establish this direct production cost as a cost per minute of print producing time. It often surprises supervision and staff alike that, even for junior staff, this figure is seldom less than 2d per minute.

Briefly then, we are building up our cost per copy by taking into account the following.

A
Machine Depreciation per annum plus
  ,,   Maintenance ,,   ,,
———————————————————— = Mcn. cost per copy
Number of copies made per annum
(Alternatively Machine Rental or Leasing Charges plus copy metering charges where applicable.)

B Copy paper cost less discount available plus wastage allowance   = Mtl. cost per copy

C
Other consumables cost per annum
——————————————— = Consumables cost per copy
Total copies per annum

D Labour cost based on measured production times for required number of copies and charged at say 2.0d per minute   = Labour cost per run

Although some of the details are only estimated, the total cost per copy now obtained is sufficiently accurate to use for purposes of comparison. However, when a decision has been made and equipment installed, it is practicable to use the figures as a temporary basis of charging if a proportional amount of overhead costs are added. It is essential to re-assess the whole area of costing when practical operating experience has been gained over a period of say, six months.

The true facts on wastage, operator ability, rate of usage of consumables, and actual quantity of copies produced will then be available.

The details of overhead costs to be included vary widely in different establishments but generally these should include a proportion of departmental supervising, clerical and distribution costs, building costs, rents, rates and taxes etc. There are also other costs which can be added directly to the charges on individual jobs on a labour plus material basis, e.g. collating, binding, etc., although in some cases it may be preferred that these are included in overhead costs.

The following examples of cost analyses of the several processes discussed, are included only as illustrations and should not be accepted as generally representative in all circumstances. They do not include any overhead costs and are based on a monthly output of around 30,000 copies per month using a machine capable of producing this quantity in each case. Variations of this production rate affect the cost in most cases and other variables may be introduced such as differing qualities of copy paper, discounts obtained, and also operator ability. In each case the labour cost includes time for reading the print order, usually about 10 to 15 seconds, and clearing finished work from the machine in addition to maintaining a suitable level of stock at the feed position. Cost of master material is included but not the cost of typing a master.

Having prepared a set of figures of this type, based on conditions prevailing at the particular site, and overhead costs added as previously indicated, it is a fairly easy exercise to prepare a price list to facilitate allocation of charges. This can often be simplified still further by analysing the pattern of work over a period. By taking the average length of run on each process and using the cost per copy for this run as the average cost per copy to be included in the price list, the clerical work in costing and charging is kept to a minimum.

APPENDIX

COST STUDIES OF OFFICE DUPLICATING PROCESSES

(All costs in pence based on 11 in. × 8½ in. copy size. Typing labour in preparing master not included.)

Spirit duplicating—direct image masters using sheet carbons

No. of copies per master	5	10	15	20	50	100
Machine depreciation and maintenance	.165	.33	.495	.66	1.65	3.3
Carbon sheet and master paper	5.0	5.0	5.0	5.0	5.0	5.0
Copy paper	1.875	3.75	5.625	7.5	18.75	37.5
Other consumables	.060	.12	.172	.24	.60	1.2
Labour set up and run	1.33	1.66	2.0	2.33	4.31	7.61
Total cost	8.430	10.86	13.292	15.73	30.31	54.61
Per copy cost	1.68	1.08	.88	.78	.61	.54

Spirit duplicating via infra-red master prepared from existing original

Duplicating costs as above but changing cost of master material (5.0d) to cost of infra-red master (7.0d), giving:—

No. of copies per master	5	10	15	20	50	100
Per copy cost	2.08	1.28	1.01	.88	.65	.57

COST STUDIES OF OFFICE DUPLICATING PROCESSES (Continued)

Stencil duplicating—direct typed stencil

No. of copies per stencil	5	10	15	20	50	100
Machine depreciation & maintenance	.5	1.0	1.5	2.0	5.0	10.0
Stencil	10.0	10.0	10.0	10.0	10.0	10.0
Copy paper	1.5	3.0	4.5	6.0	15.0	30.0
Other consumables	.125	.25	.375	.5	1.25	2.5
Labour	2.0	3.0	4.0	5.0	13.0	23.0
Total cost	14.125	17.25	20.375	23.5	44.25	75.5
Per copy cost	2.82	1.72	1.35	1.2	.88	.75

Stencil duplicating via electronic stencil prepared from existing original

Duplicating costs as above but substituting the following for the cost of the plain stencil:
Electronic Stencil:—18.0d stencil + 4.85d Scanner depreciation, maintenance and supplies + 6.0d labour + total cost 28.85d. Giving

No. of copies per stencil	5	10	15	20	50	100
Per copy cost	6.6	3.6	2.6	2.1	1.26	.944

154

COST STUDIES OF OFFICE DUPLICATING PROCESSES (Continued)

Offset litho duplicating—direct image masters

No. of copies per master	5	10	15	20	50	100
Machine depreciation & maintenance	.5	1.0	1.5	2.0	5.0	10.0
Paper master 12″ × 8½″	3.437	3.437	3.437	3.437	3.437	3.437
Copy paper	1.5	3.0	4.5	6.0	15.0	30.0
Ink, chemicals, etc.	.215	.43	.658	.86	2.15	4.3
Labour set up and run	3.5	3.5	3.5	3.5	5.5	6.5
Total cost	9.152	11.367	13.595	15.797	31.087	54.237
Per copy cost	1.83	1.13	.90	.79	.62	.54

Offset litho duplicating using an electrostatic copy master prepared from an existing original
Duplicating cost as above but inserting electrostatic master cost (5d) in lieu of plain paper master cost. Giving:

No. of copies per master	5	10	15	20	50	100
Per copy cost	2.14	1.29	1.01	.86	.66	.56

155

COST STUDIES OF OFFICE DUPLICATING PROCESSES (*Continued*)

Diazo from translucent originals

Semi-dry method using a semi-automatic machine.

No. of copies per master	5	10	15	20	50	100
Machine depreciation & maintenance	1.0	2.0	3.0	4.0	10.0	20.0
Developer, Lamp, etc.	.5	1.0	1.5	2.0	5.0	10.0
Diazo paper, med. wt.	5.0	10.0	15.0	20.0	50.0	100.0
Labour	2.5	3.5	4.5	5.5	11.5	21.5
Total cost	9.0	16.5	24.0	31.5	76.5	151.5
Per copy cost	1.8	1.65	1.6	1.57	1.53	1.52

COST STUDIES OF ADHEROGRAPHY PROCESSES

This new process to come into the category of office duplicating was first introduced on a system of charging based entirely on metering the number of copies produced by the customer. Recently this has been modified to a rental plus metering system. The rental figure is £65 per month with a £15 installation charge and copies are metered and charged at $\frac{1}{4}$d. each.

Based upon an output of 30,000 11" $\times$ 8$\frac{1}{2}$" size copies per month, the costs per copy may be established as follows.

Adherography duplicating by direct image master

No. of copies per master	5	10	15	20	50	100
Machine Rental	2.65	5.3	7.95	10.6	26.5	53.0
Direct Image Master	2.32	2.32	2.32	2.32	2.32	2.32
Copy paper	1.5	3.0	4.5	6.0	15.0	30.0
Meter charge	1.25	2.5	3.75	5.0	12.5	25.0
Powder	1.25	2.5	3.75	5.0	12.5	25.0
Labour	1.33	1.66	2.0	2.33	4.31	7.61
Total cost	10.30	17.28	24.27	31.25	73.13	142.93
Per copy cost	2.06	1.73	1.62	1.57	1.47	1.43

Adherography duplicating from existing original

Using dual spectrum master prepared on the Model 209 Copier.
Duplicating costs as above but increasing master cost from 2.32d to 4.2d.

No. of copies per master	5	10	15	20	50	100
Per copy cost	2.44	1.92	1.75	1.66	1.5	1.45

157

COST STUDIES OF THERMOFAX "SYSTEMS" PROCESSES

Thermofax "Systems" Duplicating

The number of copies it is possible to obtain from a master is limited to 25 to 30 but it is possible to make additional masters from a master by using another material Type D.

No. of copies per master	5	10	15	20
Machine hire	.12	.24	.36	.48
Master type A	4.0	4.0	4.0	4.0
Copy paper type S	9.0	18.0	27.0	36.0
Labour	2.33	3.33	4.33	5.33
Total Cost	15.45	25.57	35.69	45.81
Per copy cost	3.09	2.56	2.37	2.29

COST STUDIES OF INDIRECT ELECTROSTATIC PROCESSES

Indirect Electrostatic (Xerox 720) 20,000 copies per month

No. of copies per original	5	10	15	20
Rental	.4	.8	1.2	1.6
Meter	17.0	23.0	29.0	35.0
Paper & Consumables	3.5	7.0	10.5	14.0
Labour	2.6	4.0	5.3	6.6
Total	23.5	34.8	46.0	57.2
Per Copy Cost	4.9	3.5	3.1	2.9

Indirect Electrostatic (Xerox 2400) 30,000 copies per month

No. of copies	5	10	15	20	25	30	35
Meter	18.0	21.25	24.5	27.75	31.0	34.25	37.5
Paper } Toner	2.5	5.0	7.5	10.0	12.5	15.0	17.5
Power	.15	.3	.45	.6	.75	.9	1.05
Labour	1.1	1.43	1.6	1.84	2.1	2.33	2.6
Total Cost	21.75	27.98	34.05	40.19	46.35	52.48	58.65
Per copy Cost	4.35	2.8	2.3	2.1	1.9	1.8	1.7

159

Document copying is subject to continuous economic and technical changes. Costing exercises must therefore be carried out frequently. The actual costs of copies will vary according to local circumstances and the costs shown here are presented only to illustrate a method of arriving at relative costs.

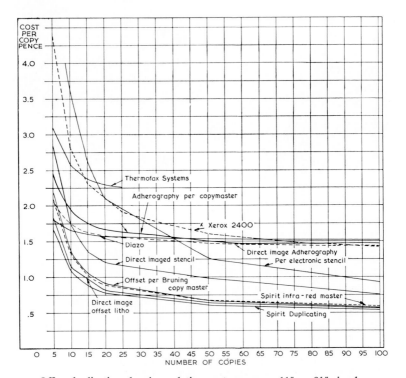

Office duplicating showing relative cost per copy 11″ × 8½″ size by the various available methods. All machine costs, supplies at list price and direct labour included. Typing masters and overheads not included.
(June 1967.)

160

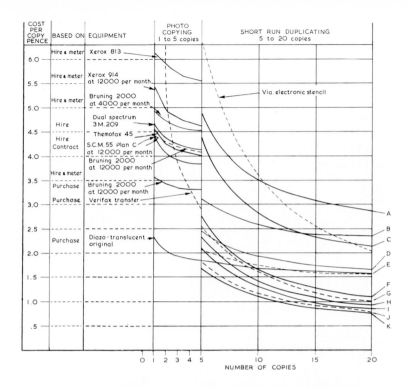

COST PER COPY PENCE	BASED ON	EQUIPMENT	PHOTO COPYING 1 to 5 copies	SHORT RUN DUPLICATING 5 to 20 copies
6.0	Hire & meter	Xerox 813		
5.5	Hire & meter	Xerox 914 at 12000 per month		Via electronic stencil
5.0	Hire & meter	Bruning 2000 at 4000 per month		
4.5	Hire	Dual spectrum 3M.209 Themofax 45		
4.0	Hire Contract / Hire & meter	S.C.M.55 Plan C at 12000 per month Bruning 2000 at 12000 per month		
3.5	Purchase	Bruning 2000 at 12000 per month		
3.0	Purchase	Verifax transfer		
2.5	Purchase	Diazo·translucent original		

NUMBER OF COPIES

Cost relationship between some photocopying methods and duplicating processes. Comparison of 11″ × 8½″ copy. All machine costs, supplies and labour included. Typing, overheads and such indirect labour as costing, collating and despatching are not included.

A. Xerox 720 at 20,000 per month. B. Thermofax systems (direct image). C. Xerox 2400 at 30,000 per month. D. Adherography via facsimile master. E. Direct image adherography (based on 30,000 metered copies per month). F. Stencil direct image. G. Litho via Xerox 914 master. H. Spirit per infra red carbon master. I. Litho via direct electrostatic copy. J. Litho via direct image papermat. K. Spirit via typed sheet carbon master. June 1967.

TECHNICAL FACILITIES OF MACHINES ESPECIALLY SUITED TO TYPEWRITER COMPOSITION

	Interchangeable fonts		Justowriter tape operated		Typebar, fixed
	Varityper	IBM72 Composers	JU Recorder	JU Reproducer	Imperial 458
No. of characters	180 in 2 fonts at a time	88 at a time	84	84	2 × 92 at a time
Unit width system	Model 720-4 ,, 565-5	9	5	5	fixed
Number of Character widths	Model 720-3 ,, 565-4	6	4	4	1
Type faces available	1140	50+	7	19	large range
Type sizes	720: 4-13 pt. 565: 4-13 pt.	7-12 pt.	12 pt only	7-14 pt	2
Special facilities	justifying mechanism; no platen; regular word spacing on justified work; quick change type fonts forms ruling device	fixed carriage; type head movement; stroke storage; quick change type fonts; retype for justification (auto on MT72 via tape) 72 Composer	punched tape with hard copy	manual or tape controlled for automatic retyping with justified margin	2 keyboards; automatic precise transfer of carriage to either. 5 variations of line spacing.
			used together for reprotyping gives 2 type face facility.		
Approx. Basic Cost (1967 pre-devaluation of sterling)	Model 720-£1771 ,, 565-£1505	£1700 MT72 Composer £8640		2 mcns. £3430	£405

Typebar machines with proportional spacing

	Executive	Raphael	Editor	Ambassador
No. of characters	86	88	88	92
Unit width system	5	3	5	4
Number of character widths	4	3	4	3
Type faces available	17	5	5	4
Type sizes	3	1	1	1
Special facilities	changeable typebars; boldening device; justifying facility; auto expand	Special paper control features; polyethylene carbon ribbon; unique typebar drive mechanism;	Auto Expander; Justifying without proof copy	all keys repeat; dual ribbon fitting. visible flying margins.
Approx. Basic Cost (1967 pre-devaluation of sterling)	£252	£220	£252	£240

163

GLOSSARY

ACTINIC LIGHT – Light mostly of violet and blue rays effective in producing photo mechanical reactions.

ALUMINIUM PLATE – Flexible printing plate used in the offset litho process.

AZO DYE – Dye formed by reaction of a diazo and coupler, as in the diazo process.

BASE MATERIAL – The paper, cloth, film or other support on which the reproduction is made.

BLANKET – A resilient rubberised blanket on to which the image is transferred from the inked lithographic plate in offset litho printing.

BLEEDING – Where the image runs off the edge of the paper, so that there is no white margin at the paper edge.

BLOCKING OUT – The use of opaque, or other means, to delete areas on a master so that they do not print.

CARBON BACKING – A carbon sheet (yellow or black) placed at back of translucent masters to provide an opaque image for contact copying.

COATING – A chemical solution, suspension or emulsion applied to the base material.

COLLATE – Assembling together in correct sequence.

CONTACT PRINTING – Printing by direct contact of a master, or of an intermediate copy, with the copy support.

CONTRAST – The density range between the extreme tones in a document or copy.

COPY – Frequently refers to a document to be reproduced (master copy) but more generally to the printed result from an original.

CURL – Tendency to coil or roll up at the edges.

DAMPING SOLUTION – The special liquid applied to a lithographic plate.

DENSITY – The light absorbing power of an image.

DEVELOPING – The action of rendering visible, by a chemical or physical process producing strong amplification, the latent image resulting from exposure of a photosensitive coating to radiation.

DIAZO BOND – A paper visually opaque but translucent to ultra violet rays.

DIAZO (DYELINE) – A process in which the print results from the effect of radiation on a diazonium sensitised material.

DIRECT-IMAGED MASTER – A duplicating or printing master upon which the image has been directly typed, written or drawn.

DISPLAY-TYPE – Comparatively large type used for headings, title pages, headlines and posters.

ELECTROPHOTOGRAPHY – Process used for producing copies through the action, on an electrically charged photosensitive semi-conducting coating, of luminous radiation which locally reduces or removes the electric charges, the image being later formed by more or less rapid precipitation on the coating of electrically charged particles.

EM – The square of the body of any size of type. Printer's unit of measurement.

ENLARGEMENT – Making to a larger scale than 1:1.

EXPOSURE – The action of submitting any sensitised surface to radiation, normally light or heat, which will act upon it to form an image or latent image.

FONT or
FOUNT – An assortment of type characters containing all letters (upper case, lower case, or both) and sometimes figures, punctuation marks and signs.
FORMAT – The size, style, shape and general appearance of any printed material.

GRAVURE – A commercial method of printing in which the image is etched in the printing plate.
GRAIN – Paper fibres lie chiefly one way giving grain direction.

HALF-TONE – A photograph which has been reproduced through a screen designed to break the transmitted image into small dots, which by variations in size, give the illusion of tonal values.
HECTOGRAPH – see spirit duplicating.
HECTOGRAPH CARBON SHEET – A specially prepared sheet of carbon used to back up a master sheet in the spirit process of hectograph duplicating.

IMAGE – A likeness of the subject matter.
INFRA-RED – Light having a longer wavelength than visible light.
INTERMEDIATE MASTER – Prepared from the original or master, and made suitable for the process to be used.

JUSTIFICATION (JUSTIFIED MARGIN) – Even right margin.

LATENT IMAGE – The image existing in a sensitised coating after exposure but before development.
LEAD – To make or widen spaces between lines of typescript.
LEADED – Separated by additional space.
LETTERPRESS – Printing from a raised surface.

LITHOGRAPHIC RIBBON – A special ribbon used for direct typing on lithographic plates.
LITHOGRAPHY – Printing from a plane surface from a greasy image on a moistened background.
LOWER CASE – Small letters of the alphabet.

MAKE READY – The time taken to prepare a duplicating machine.
MASTER – The prepared material from which copies are to be made.
MAT – A paper specially treated to receive a typed, or drawn image for reproduction by offset. Also known as a paper plate.

NEGATIVE – Having a tonal arrangement opposite to that of the original.

OFFSET-LITHOGRAPHY – A printing process in which the inked image is transferred from a printing plate to a suitably covered cylinder and then offset on to the material forming the print.
OPAQUE – Having such resistance to the passage of light as to be unsuitable for processes using transmitted light.
OPTICAL COPYING – Producing copies by means of an optical system.
OPTICAL PRINTING – Printing copies on equipment incorporating an optical system to create a latent image.

PAPER PLATE – A form of offset litho duplicating master.
PASTE-UP – Master copy made by sticking selected pieces of subject matter into a desired format; cutting, adding or deleting as necessary.
PHOTOCOPYING – Producing copies by means of luminous radiation, in general with about the same dimensions as the original.
PHOTOLETTERING – Preparing text by contact or optical printing on sensitised material.
PICA – A large printing type, a standard of printing measurement 12 points.

165

PICA-EM – Unit of measurement representing 12 points or approx. $\frac{1}{6}$ of an inch.

PITCH-TYPEWRITER – Width of a horizontal unit of space.

POINT – Printing unit of measurement, approx. $\frac{1}{72}$ of an inch.

POSITIVE – Having the same tonal arrangement as the original.

PROCESSING – The treatment of the sensitised material after exposure, revealing and retaining the image.

PROPORTIONAL SPACING – Allocation of space in the horizontal field appropriate to the width of the character.

REAM – 500 sheets of paper.

REDUCTION – Making to a smaller scale than 1:1.

REFLEX COPYING – Contact copying when radiation first passes through the copy support and is then reflected on to it by the original.

REGISTER – Exact alignment of type, especially when overlaying one image upon another.

REPROTYPING – Preparing a master typed copy suitable for preparing a duplicating or printing master by a reprographic method.

REVERSE READING – Having the image left to right as in a mirror. Also called mirror reading.

RIBBON, CARBON – A continuous strip of carbon used in all forms of typewriter.

RUN – The number of copies required from each master.

SCUM – A thin coating of ink which appears on litho plates, due to a breakdown in the de-sensitising solution.

SENSITISED – Treated so as to be sensitive to radiation, normally light or heat.

SHARPNESS – Quality of an image, characterised in particular by well marked contours, preventing confusion or ambiguity in distinguishing details.

SPIRIT DUPLICATING (HECTO-GRAPH) PROCESS – A type of duplicating which transfers the impression directly from the master to the copy by means of a fluid.

STENCIL DUPLICATING – The process employing a stencil as the reproductive medium which permits ink to pass only through the perforations forming the image.

STOCK – Printer's term for paper.

THERMIC COPYING – Photocopying by means of luminous radiation of sufficiently long wavelength, where action is mainly calorific.

TONER – In electrophotography, a developer consisting of a dispersion of pigmented particles in a carrier which may be in the form of a liquid or of a finely divided solid.

TRANSFER LETTERING – Printed characters set on a translucent carrier in such a way as to facilitate pressure transfer of selected characters to art work.

TRANSLUCENT – Permitting the passage of light, the emergent light being diffused.

TRANSPARENT – Permitting the passage of light without diffusion.

TYPOGRAPHY – The art and technique of arranging printing. Appearance, arrangement and style of reading material.

ULTRA-VIOLET – Invisible radiation having a shorter wave length than that of visible light.

UNIT-SPACING – Allocation of equal space in the horizontal field to each character irrespective of character width.

UPPER CASE – Capital letters.

INDEX

168